Contents

KU-378-879

INTRODUCTION: ONE WORLD BOOKS

The English language has not one but many forms. It is spoken with many different accents: for instance, Scots, Midlands, Northern, West Country, Cockney, Jamaican, Trinidadian, Nigerian, Australian. The list could be made much longer and readers can no doubt think of other accents to add to the list. People from different regions often use their own special words, with which other speakers of English may not be familiar. For instance, someone from north-east Scotland might ask a person to 'Dicht the table wi' a clout', or say that he or she was feeling 'wabbit', and a speaker from south-east England might be mystified as to the meaning. Alternatively, a northerner might not know the meaning of 'gimp' or a 'git'. There are other words such as 'billabong', 'boogoo', 'breeks', 'braw', 'akee' and 'takkies' which are known and used by English-speakers in some parts of the world and not in others. There are many, many more words and no doubt readers could extend the list themselves very easily.

What does this range and diversity of accent, vocabulary and usage mean? Does it mean that the English language is 'in decay', 'falling to bits', 'slipping'? Certainly not. The range and diversity of the English language are not new. They existed in the time of Chaucer, Shakespeare and Dr Samuel Johnson. Twentieth-century writers such as D. H. Lawrence (in a poem such as 'The Collier's Wife') and James Kirkup (in his autobiographical *The Only Child*) have shown how regional accents and vocabulary persisted in Nottingham and South Shields in their boyhoods. We should see such range and diversity as part of the richness of English, and they are particularly noticeable in spoken English. Because literature is about the way people think, feel and communicate with each other, good writing can convey very vividly the different rhythms of speech and the range of the spoken word. Many of the extracts and poems in this series of anthologies demonstrate just how diverse, and how satisfying, the range of spoken and written English can be.

A key feature of the English language, along with other world languages such as French, Spanish and Arabic, is that it is spoken and written by people of many races and many cultures. In many cases, as with the spread of French and Spanish, English was used as the language of government in far-flung parts of the British Empire. Consequently it began to be spoken and written by people in regions as far apart as the Indian sub-continent and the West African Gold Coast, and on islands as distant from each other as Ceylon and Barbados. English was also taken far beyond the shores of our island by settlers seeking their fortunes and a better life in Canada, Australia, New Zealand, South Africa and, earliest of all, North America. So English is a very widely used and a very cosmopolitan language. It is used for business, for government, for education, for news coverage, for everyday communication, and it is used by writers of poetry, prose and drama in an enormous number of countries scattered around the world. Most of these countries were once

THE POETRY LIBRARY
CHILDRENS SECTION

✳ TEACHING
BDCH

COPY NO.
2

ONE WORLD BOOKS

GROWING UP

EDITED BY

RHODRI JONES

Poetry Library

121467

ANTHOLOGY

WITHDRAWN FROM THE POETRY LIBRARY

HEINEMANN EDUCATIONAL BOOKS

Other titles in the One World series

One World Poets
Living Together: Four Television Plays
Moving On

Cover illustrations Teri Gower

Heinemann Educational Books Ltd
22 Bedford Square, London WC1B 3HH

LONDON   EDINBURGH   MELBOURNE   AUCKLAND
HONG KONG   SINGAPORE   KUALA LUMPUR
NEW DELHI   IBADAN   NAIROBI   JOHANNESBURG
PORTSMOUTH (NH)   KINGSTON

Selection and editorial matter © Rhodri Jones 1986

First published 1986

ISBN 0 435 10471 3

Typeset by Fakenham Photosetting Ltd, Fakenham, Norfolk
Printed and bound in Great Britain by Richard Clay (The Chaucer Press), Bungay, Suffolk

British colonies and are now members of the Commonwealth of Nations.

This series of anthologies aims to bring into British classrooms the diverse voices and 'melodies' of English from the work of a wide range of English-speaking writers. Some of them live on this island, and others speak and write in English but do not call England 'home'.

There is another very important group of writers whose work is represented in these pages. These are men and women from, in the main, the Caribbean, Africa and the Indian sub-continent who have now settled in Britain. Their contribution is often distinctive and original and their view of British life is frequently from the position of an outsider or newcomer. Their work tends to reflect particular concerns: the themes of exile and the search for identity in a new, often hostile and discriminatory, society are prominent. In some instances they draw on their experiences before coming to Britain. Their language, too, often reflects the rhythms and special vocabularies of their former homes.

Certainly the range of writing now available to English-speakers and readers of English is exciting and challenging. These anthologies are intended to make the full range of writing in English accessible to British pupils. By doing so they aim to make a strong contribution to the multi-cultural curriculum. If we can only listen to these diverse voices, tuning the English language to their own distinctive use, we will surely understand ourselves and the world so much better.

Introduction: Growing Up

This is an anthology of prose and verse related to the theme of growing up. Most of the experiences written about are typical and universal – getting lost, staying with relations, friendships and rivalries, being bullied, going to school, playing games, facing up to adult responsibilities.

However, the experience of growing up varies a great deal depending not only on your personal circumstances, but also on the particular character-istics of the society into which you are born. The following pieces show a considerable range in terms of time, place and social situation. In some, the questions of race and colour shape the experience. In 'Lost', for instance, race is present as a possible but never realized menace. In 'Rosalie', and more strongly in 'Crackling Day', racial differences are the cause of an oppressive system. Leo, the small, frail black boy who is the central figure in the passage 'Lost' by James Baldwin, loves going to the cinema and riding alone on New York's subways, but when he suddenly finds himself alone among white passengers he panics. Childhood anxieties and a society's racial arrogance are shown in 'Rosalie' by Han Suyin. Here the young girl who is half-Chinese, half-Belgian, experiences first of all her mother's indifference and later, slowly and painfully, faces the fact that in the eyes of others she and her sisters are a lesser order of people – they are 'half-castes'. Their Chinese blood is a disadvantage even in Peking – at that time a city dominated by aggressive warlords and nervous European powers. Lee, in 'Crackling Day' by Peter Abrahams, hits back at white boys who insult his dead father. He pays dearly for his courage when the boys and their father, who is his uncle's boss, demand that he is punished.

The loneliness and insecurity sometimes experienced in childhood are explored in Anita Desai's 'Twilight Games', and Dannie Abse's 'What's It Like To Be Jewish?' sets out in a humorous yet painful way how a boy comes to terms with belonging, always, to a minority group set apart from the majority. Bonds established in childhood across class and racial lines are sensitively explored in Ian McDonald's 'Friendship'.

School, its comedy, its pain and its different kinds of enjoyment, features in a number of passages. Emlyn Williams's 'George' describes how a young Welsh-speaking boy comes to grips first with English, and then with French, helped by a 'thirty-four-year-old dynamo' of a teacher. G. B. Edwards's account describes how he skipped his stifling Sunday-school classes in Guernsey, managing, skilfully, to keep his parents ignorant of the fact. On a more sombre note, the shock of a sudden bereavement is described in an extract from Edna O'Brien's *The Country Girls*. Caithleen, while enjoying an outing in an Irish country town, learns that her mother has died. In the long narrative poem 'David', by Earle Birney, the hero has to come to terms with physical danger and make a painful and difficult decision.

The extracts (and the single short story) that have been chosen represent the work of writers from a range of countries and cultures. The styles of their writing also vary greatly – from the emotion-filled prose of the black American James Baldwin, to the wild farce of Salman Rushdie, the Indian writer now living in Britain; from the dialect undertones of the Guernsey writer G. B. Edwards to the racy, colourful language of Dannie Abse as he depicts the life of a Jewish boy in a Welsh environment.

Poetry can often pinpoint an experience with great vividness and economy. Thus Edward Lucie-Smith's 'A Tropical Childhood' describes the false security of childhood, when you are unaware of the dangers that lie ahead, outside your small, bright world. Brathwaite's 'Dives' suggests the ignorance, innocence and enjoyment of boys diving, sometimes dangerously, for coins tossed to them by wealthy passing tourists. Seamus Heaney's three poems touch on different aspects of growing up. His well-known 'Death of a Naturalist' shows how enthusiasm for a particular interest can evaporate in the face of the unexpected; 'The Barn' suggests the fascination and fear of the dark and the unknown; and his 'Mid-Term Break' describes his own experience of early bereavement when his young brother is killed by a car. Death, danger and friendship are all linked in Earle Birney's long narrative poem 'David'.

Through the work and varied experiences of this group of writers we hope first to highlight in a new way, through drawing on a range of writers from different cultures, the complex world of childhood. Second, we hope that the pieces in this anthology will stimulate pupils to examine their own lives afresh and look with sharpened eyes at their own families, their friends and their surroundings – and write about their own experiences of growing up.

ACKNOWLEDGEMENTS

The editor and publishers wish to thank the following for permission to reproduce copyright material:

Michael Joseph Ltd and James Baldwin for 'Lost' from 'Tell Me How Long the Train's Been Gone'; André Deutsch Ltd and Merle Hodge for 'Staying with Ma' from Crick Crack Monkey © 1981; William Heinemann Ltd for the extract from Games at Twilight by Anita Desai; Faber & Faber Ltd for 'Crackling Day' from Tell Freedom by Peter Abrahams; William Heinemann Ltd for 'The Marbleus' from Humming Bird Tree by Ian McDonald; Longman Ltd for 'Lee, Coloured' from African Poetry for Schools by Peter Abrahams; Edward Lucie-Smith for the extract from A Tropical Childhood © 1981 Edward Lucie-Smith; Oxford University Press for 'Dives' from Other Exiles (1975) by Edward Kamau Brathwaite; Vallentine, Mitchell & Co. Ltd for 'What's It Like to be Jewish?' from Ash on a Young Man's Sleeve by Dannie Abse; Han Suyin and Jonathan Cape Ltd for 'Rosalie' from The Crippled Tree; Faber & Faber Ltd for 'Death of a Naturalist', 'The Barn' and 'Mid-Term Break' from Selected Poems by Seamus Heaney; Hamish Hamilton for 'Guernsey Childhood' from The Book of Ebenezer le Page by G. B. Edwards © 1981 by Edward P. de G. Chaney; Emlyn Williams and Hamish Hamilton for 'Moving On' from George; Salman Rushdie and Jonathan Cape Ltd for 'The Mutilations of Saleem' from Midnight's Children; Edna O'Brien for 'Last Day of Childhood' from The Country Girls; Earle Birney and McClelland & Stewart for 'David' from Earle Birney's Collected Poems.

They also thank the following for supplying photographs of authors:

Michael Joseph Ltd for James Baldwin; Jonathan Cape Ltd for Han Suyin; Tara Heinemann for Edward Lucie-Smith; Jonathan Cape Ltd and Isolde Ohlbaum for Salman Rushdie; William Heinemann Ltd for Ian MacDonald; Jonathan Cape Ltd for Edna O'Brien; Faber & Faber Ltd for Seamus Heaney; Faber & Faber Ltd and Amäaor Packer for Peter Abrahams. The photograph of Emlyn Williams was supplied courtesy of Planned Theatre Ltd.

Illustrations were supplied by the following:

Emily Booth, pages 10, 50, 74, 81; Henry Iles, pages 48, 95; John Morris, pages 17, 70, 88; Adrian Thomas, pages 25, 53, 104; Mark Urgent, pages 1, 58; Trevor Waugh, page 36.

We also acknowledge the following sources of photographs:

Barbados Board of Tourism, page 52; British Library, page 19; Keith Cardwell, page 65; Celtic Picture Agency, page 85; Satour, page 27; Carel Toms, page 79.

JAMES BALDWIN

James Baldwin was born in Harlem, New York City, in 1924. He left DeWitt Clinton High School in 1941 and spent the next six years doing a variety of jobs before going to Paris in 1948. He lived in Paris until 1957 when he returned to the United States and soon established a reputation as one of the most able and articulate supporters of the rights of black Americans.

Baldwin has written novels, plays and short stories, a number of which explore and speak out against racism in the United States. His best-known novels are *Another Country* and *Go Tell It on the Mountain*. In *Tell Me How Long the Train's Been Gone* (from which this extract is taken), Leo Proudhammer, a famous black actor, looks back over his life.

The extract here is from his difficult, and in some ways dangerous, childhood in Harlem. When Leo cannot find an adult to accompany him into the cinema he wanders the streets and travels on the maze of subways, sometimes with unexpected results.

LOST

The hall was dark, smelling of cooking, of boiling diapers,[1] of men and boys pissing there late at night, of stale wine, of rotting garbage. The walls were full of an information which I could scarcely read and did not know how to use. We dropped down the stairs, Caleb going two at a time, pausing at each landing, briefly, to glance back up at me. I dropped down behind him as fast as I could. Sometimes Caleb was in a bad mood and then everything I did was wrong. But when Caleb was in a good mood, it didn't matter that everything I did was wrong. When I reached the street level, Caleb was already on the stoop,[2] joking with some of his friends, who were standing in the doorway – who seemed always to be in the doorway, no matter what hour one passed through. I didn't like Caleb's friends because I was afraid of them. I knew the only reason they didn't try to make life hell for me the way they made life hell for a lot of the other kids was because they were afraid of Caleb. I came through the door, passing between my brother and his friends, down to the sidewalk, feeling, as they looked briefly at me and then continued joking with Caleb, what they felt: that here was Caleb's round-eyed, frail and useless sissy of a little brother. They pitied Caleb for having to take me out. On the other hand, they also wanted to go to the show, but didn't have the money. Therefore, in silence, I could crow over them even as they despised me. But this was always a terribly risky, touch and go business, for Caleb might always, at any moment, and with no warning, change his mind and drive me away, and, effectively, take their side against me. I always stood, those Saturday afternoons, in fear and trembling, holding on to the small shield of my bravado, while waiting for Caleb to come down the steps of the stoop, to come down the steps, away from his friends, to me. I prepared myself, always, for the moment when he would turn to me, saying, 'Okay, kid. You run along. I'll see you later.'

This meant that I would have to go to the movies by myself and hang around in front of the box-office, waiting for some grown-up to take me in. I could not go back upstairs, for this would be informing my mother and father that Caleb had gone off somewhere – after promising to take me to the movies. Neither could I simply hang around the block, playing with the kids on the block. For one thing, my demeanour, as I came out of the house, those Saturdays, very clearly indicated that I had better things to do than play with *them*; for another, they were not terribly anxious to play with *me*; and, finally, my remaining on the block would have had exactly the same effect as my going upstairs. Someone would surely inform my father and mother, or they might simply look out of the window, or one of them would come downstairs to buy something they had forgotten while shopping, or my father would pass down the block on his way to the bar. In short, to remain on the block after Caleb's dismissal was to put myself at the mercy of the block and to put Caleb at the mercy of our parents.

So I prepared myself, those Saturdays, to respond with a cool, 'Okay. See you later,' and prepared myself then to turn indifferently away, and walk. This was surely the most terrible moment. The moment I turned away I was committed, I was trapped, and I then had miles to walk, so it seemed to me, before I would be out of sight, before the block ended and I could turn on to the avenue. I wanted to run out of that block, but I never did. I never looked back. I forced myself to walk very slowly, looking neither right nor left, trying to look neither up nor down – striving to seem at once distracted and offhand; concentrating on the cracks in the sidewalks, and stumbling over them, trying to whistle, feeling every muscle in my body, from my pigeon toes to my jiggling behind, to my burning neck; feeling that all the block was watching me, and feeling – which was odd – that I deserved it. And then I reached the avenue, and turned, still not looking back, and was released from those eyes at least, but now faced other eyes, eyes coming towards me. These eyes were the eyes of children stronger than me, who would steal my movie money; these eyes were the eyes of white cops, whom I feared, whom I hated with a literally murderous hatred; these eyes were the eyes of old folks who also thought I was a sissy and who might wonder what I was doing on this avenue by myself. And these eyes were the eyes of men and women going in and out of bars, or standing on the corners, who certainly had no eyes for me, but who occupied the centre of my bewildered attention because they seemed, at once, so abject and so free.

And then I got to the show. Sometimes, someone would take me in right away and sometimes I would have to wait. I looked at the posters which seemed magical indeed to me in those days. I was very struck, not altogether agreeably, by the colours. The faces of the movie stars were in red, in green, in blue, in purple, not at all like the colours of real faces and yet they looked more real than real. Or, rather, they looked like faces far from me, faces which I would never be able to decipher, faces which could be seen but never changed or touched, faces which existed only behind these doors. I don't know what I thought. Some great assault, certainly, was being made on my imagination, on my sense of reality. Caleb could draw, he was teaching me to draw, and I wondered if he could teach me to draw faces like these. I looked at the stills from the show, seeing people in attitudes of danger, in attitudes of love, in attitudes of sorrow and loss. They were not like any people I had ever seen and this made them, irrevocably, better. With one part of my mind, of course, I knew that here was James Cagney – holding his gun like a prize;

and here was Clark Gable, all dimples, teeth, and eyes, the eyes filled with a smoky, taunting recollection of his invincible virility; here was Joan Crawford, gleaming with astonishment, and here was proud, quivering Katherine Hepburn, who could never be astonished, and here was poor, down-trodden Sylvia Sidney, weeping in the clutches of yet another gangster. But only the faces and the attitudes were real, more real than the lives we led, more real than our days and nights, and the names were merely brand-names, like Campbell's Baked Beans or Kellogg's Corn Flakes. We went to see James Cagney because we had grown accustomed to that taste, we knew that we would like it.

But, then, I would have to turn my attention from the faces and the stills and watch the faces coming to the box-office. And this was not easy, since I didn't, after all, want everyone in the neighbourhood to know that I was loitering outside the movie house waiting for someone to take me in, exactly like an orphan. If it came to our father's attention, he would kill both Caleb and me. Eventually, I would see a face which looked susceptible and which I did not know. I would rush up beside him or her – but it was usually a man, for they were less likely to be disapproving – and whisper 'Take me in' and give him my dime.[3] Sometimes the man simply took the dime and disappeared into the movies, sometimes he gave my dime back to me and took me in, anyway. Sometimes I ended up wandering around the streets – but I couldn't wander into a strange neighbourhood because I would be beaten up if I did – until I figured the show was out. It was dangerous to get home too early and, of course, it was practically lethal to arrive too late. If all went well, I could cover for Caleb, saying that I had left him with some boys on the stoop. Then, if *he* came in too late and got a dressing down for it, it could not be considered my fault.

But if wandering around this way was not without its dangers, neither was it without its discoveries and delights. I discovered subways – I discovered, that is, that I could ride on subways by myself, and, furthermore, that I could usually ride for nothing. Sometimes, when I ducked under the turnstile, I was caught and cuffed and turned back, and sometimes great black ladies seized on me as a pretext for long, very loud, ineffably moral lectures about wayward children breaking their parents' hearts; as to this, however, the ladies very often and very loudly disagreed among themselves, insisting that wayward children were produced by wayward parents, and calling down on the heads of my parents the most vivid penalties that heaven could devise. And heaven would have had to go some to have surpassed their imaginations. Sometimes, doing everything in my power not to attract their attention, I endeavoured to look as though I were the charge of a respectable-looking man or woman, entering the subway in their shadow, and sitting very still beside them. It was best to try and sit *between* two such people, for, then, each would automatically assume that I was with the other. There I would sit, then, in a precarious anonymity, watching the people, listening to the roar, watching the lights and the cables and the lights of other stations flash by. It seemed to me that nothing was faster than a subway train and I loved the speed because the speed was dangerous. For a time, during these expeditions, I simply sat and watched the people. Lots of people would be dressed up, for this was Saturday night. The women's hair would be all straightened and curled and the lipstick on their full lips looked purple and make-believe against the dark skins of their faces. They wore very fancy capes or coats, in wonderful colours, and long dresses, and sometimes they had jewels in their hair and sometimes they wore flowers on their dresses. They were almost as beautiful as movie stars. And so the men with them seemed to think. The hair of the men was slick and wavy, brushed up into pompadours; or they wore very sharp hats, brim flicked down dangerously over one eye, with perhaps one flower in the lapel of their many-coloured suits and a tie-pin shining in the centre of their bright ties. Their hands were large and very clean, with rings on their heavy fingers, and their nails glowed. They laughed and talked with their girls, but quietly, for there were white people in the car. The white people would scarcely ever be dressed up, and never as brilliantly as the coloured people. They wore just ordinary suits and hats and coats and did not speak to each other at all – only read their papers and stared at the advertisements. But they fascinated me more than the coloured people did because I knew nothing at all about them and could not imagine what they were like.

Their faces were as strange to me as the faces on the movie posters and the stills, but far less attractive because, mysteriously, menacing, and, under the ruthless subway light, were revealed literally, in their true colours, which were not green, red, blue, or purple, but a mere, steady, unnerving, pinkish reddish yellow. I wondered why people called them white – they certainly were not white. Black people were not black, either – my father was wrong. Underground, I received my first apprehension of New York neighbour-hoods, and, underground, first felt what may be called a civic terror. I very soon realized that after the train had passed a certain point, going uptown or downtown, all the coloured people disappeared. The first time I realized this, I panicked and got lost. I rushed off the train, terrified of what these white people might do to me with no coloured person around to protect me – even to scold me, even to beat me; at least their touch was familiar, and I knew that they did not, after all, intend to kill me – and got on another train only because I saw a black man on it. But almost everyone else was white. The train did not stop at any of the stops I remembered. I became more and more frightened, frightened of getting off the train and frightened of staying on it, frightened of saying anything to the man and frightened that he would get off the train before I *could* say anything to him. He was my salvation and he stood there in the unapproachable and frightening form that salvation so often takes. At each stop, I watched him with despair. To make matters worse, I suddenly realized that I had to pee; once I realized it, this need became a torment; the horror of wetting my pants in front of all these people made the torment greater. Finally, I tugged at the man's sleeve. He looked down at me with a gruff, amused concern – he had been staring out of the dark window, far away with his own thoughts; then, reacting, no doubt, to the desperation in my face, he bent closer. I asked him if there was a bathroom on the train. He laughed.

'No,' he said, 'but there's a bathroom in the station.' He looked at me again. 'Where're you going?'

I told him that I was going home. But the pressure on my bladder made it hard for me to speak. The train looked like it was never going to stop.

'And where's home?'

I told him. This time he did not laugh.

'Do you know where you are?'

I shook my head. At that moment the train came into the station and after several hours it rolled to a stop. After a slightly longer time than that, the jammed doors opened and the man led me to the bathroom. I ran in, and I hurried because I was afraid he would disappear. But I was glad he had not come in with me.

When I came out, he stood waiting for me. 'Now,' he said, 'you in Brooklyn – you ever hear of Brooklyn? What you doing out here by yourself?'

'I got lost,' I said.

'I *know* you got lost. What I want to know is how *come* you got lost? Where's your Mama? where's your Daddy?'

I almost said that I didn't have any because I liked his face and his voice and was half hoping to hear him say that *he* didn't have any little boy and would just as soon take a chance on me. But I told him that my Mama and Daddy were at home.

'And do they know where *you* are?'

I said, 'No.' There was a pause.

'Well, I know they going to make your tail hot when they see you.' He took my hand. 'Come on.'

And he led me along the platform and then down some steps and along a narrow passage and then up some steps on to the opposite platform. I was very impressed by this manoeuvre, for, in order to accomplish the same purpose, I had always left the subway station and gone up into the streets. Now that the emergency was over (and I knew that I would not be late getting home) I was in no great hurry to leave my saviour; but I didn't know how to say this, the more particularly as he seemed to be alternating between amusement and irritation. I asked him if he had a little boy.

'Yes,' he said, 'and if you was *my* little boy, I'd paddle your behind so you couldn't sit down for a week.'

I asked him how old was his little boy and what was his name and if his little boy was at home.

'He *better* be at home!' He looked at me and laughed. 'His name is Jonathan. He ain't but five years old.' His gaze refocused, sharpened. 'How old are you?'

I told him I was ten, going on eleven.

'You a pretty bad little fellow,' he said, then.

I tried to look repentant, but I would not have dreamed of denying it.

'Now, look here,' he said, 'this here's the uptown side – can you read or don't you never go to school?' I assured him that I could read. 'Now, to get where you going, you got to change trains.' He told me where. 'Here, I'll write it down for you.' He found some paper in his pockets, but no pencil. We heard the train coming. He looked about him in helpless annoyance, looked at his watch, looked at me. 'It's all right, I'll tell the conductor.'

But the conductor, standing between the two cars, had rather a mean pink face and my saviour looked at him dubiously. 'He *might* be all right. But we better not take no chances.' He pushed me ahead of him into the train. 'You know you right lucky that *I* got a little boy? If I didn't, I swear I'd just let you go on and *be* lost. You don't know the kind of trouble you going to get me in at home. My wife ain't *never* going to believe *this* story.'

I told him to give me his name and address and that I would write a letter to his wife and to his little boy, too. This caused him to laugh harder than ever. 'You only say that because you know I ain't got no pencil. You are one *hell* of a shrewd little boy.'

I told him that then maybe we should get off the train and that I would go back home with him. This made him grave.

'What does your father do?' This question made me uneasy. I stared at him for a long time before I answered. 'He works in a' – I could not pronounce the word – 'he has a job.'

He nodded. 'I see. Is he home now?'

I really did not know and I said I did not know.

'And what does your mother do?'

'She stays home. But she goes out to work – sometimes.'

Again he nodded. 'You got any brothers or sisters?'

I told him: 'No.'

'I see. What's your name?'

'Leo.'

'Leo what?'

'Leo Proudhammer.'

He saw something in my face.

'What do you want to be when you grow up, Leo?'

'I want to be' – and I had never said this before – 'I want to be a – a movie actor. I want to be a – actor.'

'You pretty skinny for that,' he said.

But I certainly had, now, all of his attention.

'That's all right,' I told him, 'Caleb's going to teach me to swim. That's how you get big.'

'Who's Caleb?'

I opened my mouth, I stared at him, I started to speak, I checked myself – as the train roared into a station. He glanced out of the window, but did not move. 'He swims,' I said.

'Oh,' he said, after a very long pause, during which the doors slammed and the train began to move. 'Is he a good swimmer?'

I said that Caleb was the best swimmer in the world.

'Okay,' my saviour said, 'okay,' and put his hand on my head again, and smiled at me. I asked him what his name was. 'Charles,' he said, 'Charles Williams. But you better call me *Uncle* Charles, you little devil, because you have certainly ruined my Saturday night.'

I told him (for I knew it) that it was still early.

'It ain't going to be early,' he said, 'by the time I get back home.' The train came into the station. 'Here's where we change,' he said.

We got out of the train and crossed the platform and waited.

'Now,' he said, 'this train stops exactly where you going. Tell me where you going.'

I stared at him.

'I want you,' he said, 'to tell me exactly where you *going*. I can't be fooling with you all night.'

I told him.

'You sure that's right?'

I told him I was sure.

'I got a very good memory,' he said. 'Give me your address. Just say it, I'll remember it.'

So I said it, staring into his face as the train came roaring in.

'If you don't go straight home,' he said, 'I'm going to come and see your daddy and when we find you, you'll be mighty sorry.' He pushed me into the train and put one shoulder against the door. 'Go on, now,' he said, loud enough for all the car to hear, 'your mama'll meet you at the station where I told you to get off.' He repeated my subway stop, pushed the angry door with his shoulder, and then said, gently, 'Sit down, Leo.' And he remained in the door until I sat down. 'So long, Leo,' he said, then, and stepped backward, out. The doors closed. He grinned at me and waved and the train began to move. I waved back. Then he was gone, the station was gone, and I was on my way back home.

I never saw that man again but I made up stories in my head about him, I dreamed about him, I even wrote a letter to him and his wife and his little boy, but I never mailed it. I had a feeling that he would not like my father and that my father would not like him. And since Caleb never liked anyone *I* liked, I never mentioned him to Caleb.

GLOSSARY
1 *diapers*: nappies.
2 *stoop*: platform or veranda at front of a house.
3 *dime*: small American coin worth 10 cents. Here the price of a cinema ticket.

SUGGESTIONS FOR WRITING AND DISCUSSION

1 *Describe the relationship Leo had with his brother Caleb.*
2 *What were Leo's feelings about the movies and movie stars?*
3 *What were Leo's feelings about white people?*
4 *What were Leo's feelings about the man, and what impression do you get of him?*
5 *Describe the kind of boy Leo was and the way he spent his Saturdays.*
6 *Comment on the style in which this extract is written. (For instance, how Leo uses repetitions for effect, his descriptions of people, the way he introduces dialogue and the way he introduces his own thoughts.)*
7 *'I dreamed about him, I even wrote a letter to him and his wife and his little boy, but I never mailed it.' Write your version of Leo's letter to the man, his wife and little boy. Write the man's answer.*
8 *Some adults are much kinder and more sympathetic to children than others. Write a description of someone you knew (or still know) who showed kindness and sympathy to you.*

FURTHER READING

Go Tell It on the Mountain James Baldwin (Corgi)
Another Country James Baldwin (Corgi)
Tell Me How Long the Train's Been Gone James Baldwin (Michael Joseph)
If Beale Street Could Talk James Baldwin (Michael Joseph)

MERLE HODGE

Merle Hodge was born in Trinidad in 1944. After winning the prestigious Trinidad and Tobago Girls' Island Scholarship in 1962 she went to England and studied French at University College, London. She has travelled widely and has spent long periods in France and Denmark and has also visited Italy, Spain, Germany, Russia, Senegal and the United States. She has translated a collection of poems by the French Guyanese poet Léon Damas. She was until recently a lecturer in French at the University of the West Indies in Jamaica, and she has taught in high schools and worked in education in Trinidad and Grenada.

Her novel *Crick Crack Monkey* is about a young girl, Tee, growing up in Trinidad. Tee

spends her early and happiest years with her poor aunt, Tantie. But later, after she wins a scholarship, she has to live in a very different world with her rich and snobbish Aunt Beatrice. In the passage below

Tantie is afraid that Aunt Beatrice will take the young Tee away from her by force so she has sent her, together with her small brother, to stay with their grandmother, by the sea.

STAYING WITH MA

The very next day we were being hustled off to Ma, away away up in Pointe d'Espoir, with Toddan falling asleep on Mikey's lap as usual and Mikey having to climb the track with him over one shoulder and the suitcase in the other hand. When we came back it would be time for me to go to school, and Toddan they could simply lose among Neighb' Ramlaal-Wife's own when there was no one at home.

The August holidays had already begun, so that all the multitude was there. Our grandmother was a strong, bony woman who did not smile unnecessarily, her lower jaw set forward at an angle that did not brook opposition or argument. She did not use up too many words at a time either, except when she sat on the step with us teeming around her, when there was a moon, and told us 'nancy-stories.[1] If the night was too dark or if it was raining there was no story-telling – it was inconceivable to her that one should sit inside a house and tell 'nancy-stories. At full moon there was a bonus and then we would light a black-sage[2] fire for the mosquitoes and sand-flies and the smoke smelt like contented drowsiness. And when at the end of the story she said 'Crick crack?' our voices clambered over one another in the gleeful haste to chorus back in what ended on an untidy shrieking crescendo:

Monkey break 'e back
On a rotten pommerac![3]

And there was no murmur of protest when she ordered with finality: 'That is enough. Find allyu bed.'

On most afternoons we descended to the beach in a great band, Ma saluting houses on the way:

'Oo-oo Ma-Henrietta!'

'Oo-oo!' a voice would answer from the depths of the house or from somewhere in the backyard.

'Is me an' mih gran's passin'.'

'Right, Ma-Josephine!'

Ma brought with her a wooden box and a stick. While we splashed about in the water she sat immobile and straight-backed on her box, her hands resting together on the stick which she held upright in front of her. When someone started to venture too far out she rapped sharply on the box with the stick. And when it was time to go she rapped again: 'Awright. Come-out that water now!'

Then we walked along the sand, straggled and zig-zagged and played along the sand, to where they drew the nets in, and we 'helped' in this latter operation, fastening ourselves like a swarm of bees to the end of the rope and adding as much to the total effort as would a swarm of bees bunched at the end of the thick hauling-rope. Afterwards we swooped down and collected the tiny fishes that they left on the beach, and Ma let us roast these in the fire at home.

Ma's land was to us an enchanted country, dipping into valley after valley, hills thickly covered with every conceivable kind of foliage, cool green dark-nesses, sudden little streams that must surely have been squabbling past in the days when Brar Anancy and Brar Leopard[4] and all the others roamed the earth outsmarting each other. And every now and then we would lose sight of the sea and then it would come into sight again down between trees when you least expected to see it, and always, it seemed, in a different direction; that was frightening too. We went out with Ma to pick fruit, she armed with a cut-lass with which she hacked away thick vines and annihilated whole bushes in one swing. We returned with our baskets full of oranges, mangoes, chen-nettes, Ma bent under a bunch of plantains that was more than half her size.

Ma had a spot in the market on Sunday mornings, and she spent a great part of the week stewing cashews, pommes-cythères, cerises, making guava-cheese and guava jelly, sugar-cake, nut-cake, bennay-balls, toolum, shaddock-peel candy, chilibibi. . . . On these days we hung slyly about the kitchen, if only to feed on the smells; we were never afforded the opportunity of gorging ourselves – we partook of these delicacies when Ma saw fit, and not when we desired. She was full of maxims for our edification, of which the most baffling and maddening was:

> *Who ask*
> *don't get*
> *Who don't ask*
> *don't want*
> *Who don't want*
> *don't get*
> *Who don't get*
> *don't care*

For her one of the cardinal sins of childhood was gluttony: 'Stuff yu guts today an' eat the stones of the wilderness tomorrow.' (Ma's sayings often began on a note of familiarity only to rise into an impressive incomprehensibility, or vice versa, as in 'Them that walketh in the paths of corruption will live to ketch dey arse.')

She was equal to all the vagaries of childhood. Nothing took her by surprise – she never rampaged, her initial reaction was always a knowing 'Hm'. Not that one permitted oneself the maximum of vagaries in Ma's house – her eye was too sharp and her hand too quick. But there were the odd times that somebody thought she wasn't looking. Sometimes there would be a chase, exciting but brief, when the culprit was hauled back panting to face the music in front of us all. Sometimes he was merely set free again, since he was already frightened to death and would certainly never try that one again.

Just as there were enough of us to play Hoop and Rescue and every conceivable game, so there were enough of us for the occasional outbreak of miniature gang-warfare. We sat for hours under the house in two camps proffering hearty insults. The division usually fell between those who were kept by Ma and those of us who didn't really live there. Ma's children were the 'bush-monkeys' and 'country-bookies' and they in turn made it known to us how deep was their longing for the day when we would all depart so they could have their house and their yard and their land to themselves again. This stung deep for though we knew beyond doubt that it was equally our house and yard and land yet it was those fiends who lived in the house all year round and played in the yard and went on expeditions into the land with Ma when we were not there. If hostilities lasted till a mealtime, then we placed ourselves on opposite sides of the table and eyed each other with contempt. And if they lasted until night-time, then going to bed was an uncomfortable affair, for it took rather longer to fall asleep when every muscle of your body and every inch of your concentration was taut with the effort of not touching your neighbour. But we the vacation batch always had our revenge when it was time to go home and our big-people had come to fetch us and we were all dressed up for the trip home and being fussed over – Ma's children looked a little envious then.

Ma awoke every morning with a groan quickly routed by a brief loud cheups.[5] She rose at a nameless hour and in my half-sleep I saw a mountain shaking off mist in one mighty shudder and the mist falling away in little drops of cloud. The cheups with which Ma greeted the day expressed her essential attitude before the whole of existence – what yu mus' beat-up yuself for? In the face of the distasteful and unavoidable, the unexpected and irreversible, all that Ma could not crush or confound with a barked word or surmount with her lioness strength, she reacted to with a cheups, more or less loud, more or less long. Thus she sucked her teeth loudly and without further comment when the iron pot full of rice spitefully tipped itself over into the fire; when the sun took to playing monkey-wedding[6] with the rain the moment she had put the final clothes-peg to her miles of washing strung from the breadfruit tree to the zaboca tree, from the zaboca tree to the house-post and from the house-post to the chicken-run post, Ma sucked her teeth and turned her back.

And there were the days of real rain. We could see it coming, down across the water, a dark ceiling letting down slow grey streamers into the horizon (that was God pee-peeing into his posie) and then it would be pounding the earth like a thousand horses coming at us through the trees. It was frightening and exciting. A sudden greyness had descended upon everything and we had seconds in which to race about the yard like mad-ants helping Ma to place her assortment of barrels and buckets in places where they would catch the water. And all the time the rain pounding nearer, racing to catch us. When the first messenger spray hit us there was pandemonium – we stampeded into the house, some squealing with a contagious excitement. We ran round shutting the windows, pulling out buckets and basins to place under the leaks, still squealing and colliding with each other. As the windows were closed one by one a cosy darkness crept in, and we felt as if our numbers were growing. We all collected into one room. Sometimes we piled on to the big-bed and made a tent of the coverlets, tying them to the four posts of the bed. Under the tent the commotion was sustained, rising to squealing pitch at every flash of lightning and crack of thunder, or every time the tent collapsed about us, or when a lath fell so that a part of the bed caved in under some of us; or when someone chose this situation of inescapable intimacy to emit an anonymous but very self-assertive poops. It was impossible to detect the owner, and chaos ensued while every man accused his immediate neighbour. In the end we had to count the culprit out by means of Ink-Pink-Mamma-Stink, and the man thus denounced was emitted bodily amidst a new burst of commotion.

Meanwhile Ma bustled about the house – we knew that she was just as excited as we were, barricaded into the darkened house with the rain drumming on the galvanize[7] and surrounding us with heavy purring like a huge mother-cat. Ma seemed to be finding things to do so as not to yield to the temptation to come and crawl under the sheets and play tent with us. Then she came in with a big plate of sugar-cake and guava-cheese, and pretended to be scandalized at the way we were treating the bedclothes.

And when the rain had stopped we dressed up in Grampa's old jackets and went out with Ma to look at the river. This was like a ritual following upon the rain – she had to go and see the river. We walked behind her squelching joyously in the new puddles and mud. The air smelt brown and green, like when the earth was being made. From a long way off the river was calling to us through the trees, in one continuous groan, so that when we finally came to it, wet and splashed from the puddles and from the bushes we had brushed against, it was as though we had been straining along in it the whole time. Ma stopped abruptly and spread out both her arms to stop us, as though it were likely that we would keep on walking right into the fast ochre water. We counted how many trees it had risen past on the bank. If the river came down every week Ma's rapture would be quite as new.

'Eh!' she exclaimed, and then fell back into her trance. Then a little later on 'Eh!' shaking her head from side to side, 'Well yes, well yes!' We stood around her in an unlikely silence like spattered acolites in our jumble-sale clothes, in the bright air hanging out crisp and taut to dry, and the river ploughing off with the dirt and everything drenched and bowing and satisfied and resting before the world started up again from the beginning.

*

We roamed the yard and swarmed down to the water and played hoop around the breadfruit tree as if we would always be wiry-limbed children whose darting about the sun would capture like amber and fix into eternity. Although Ma exclaimed upon our arrival each year at how big we'd got, yet all the holidays at Pointe d'Espoir were one August month, especially in the middle part of the day when everything seemed to set in the still, hanging brightness – our games and squabbling; the hens with their heads down scratching about the yard; the agreeableness of sitting clamped between Ma's knees having one's hair plaited. The cream air in the middle part of the day was like Time staring at itself in a mirror, the two faces locked dreamily in an eternal gaze.

I was Ma's own-own bold-face Tee, harden' as the Devil's shit but that is yu great great grandmother, that is she, t'ank Gord. Sometimes when the others were not about she would accost me suddenly: 'An who is Ma sugar-cake?'

'Tee!'

'An who is Ma dumplin'?'

'Tee!'

And all at once she put on an expression of mock-displeasure and snapped at me gruffly: 'Who tell yu that?'

'Ma tell mih!'

'Well Ma is a liard ol'-fool'; and she thrust a hunk of guava-cheese at me.

Ma said that I was her grandmother come back again. She said her grandmother was a tall straight proud woman who lived to an old old age and her eyes were still bright like water and her back straight like bamboo, for all the heavy-load she had carried on her head all her life. The People[8] gave her the name Euphemia or Euph-something, but when they called her that she used to toss her head like a horse and refuse to answer so they'd had to give up in the end and call her by her true-true name.

Then Ma creased her forehead and closed her eyes and rubbed her temples and if anyone spoke she waved her hand with irritation. She sat like this for a long time. Then she would shake her head sorrowfully. She couldn't remember her grandmother's true-true name. But Tee was growing into her grandmother again, her spirit was in me. They'd never bent down her spirit and she would come back and come back and come back; if only she could live to see Tee grow into her tall proud straight grandmother.

GLOSSARY

1 *'nancy stories*: Anancy was, and is, the spider-man hero of many of the folk tales of West Africa, in particular Ghana. The Anancy stories were taken to the West Indies over centuries by African people who were forcibly transported from the West African coast to work as slaves in the sugar plantations there.

2 *black-sage*: a low-growing bush whose wood is burned to repel insects.

3 *pommerac*: a tree also known as Malay Apple. It has large, shiny green leaves and deep pink blossoms. It has pink and white edible fruit.

4 *Brar Anancy ... Brar Leopard*: heroes of folk tales.

5 *cheups*: a sucking sound denoting disgust.

6 *playing monkey-wedding*: a term used to describe the weather when it rains in the middle of bright sunshine.
7 *galvanize*: metal roof.
8 *The People*: the white plantation-owners.

SUGGESTIONS FOR WRITING AND DISCUSSION

1 *What were the attractions of staying with her grandmother (Ma) for Tee?*
2 *Describe the relationship between the children Ma kept and the visitors.*
3 *How does the writer convey the happiness of those August months? (Notice, for instance, her description of the games they played, the places visited and the place itself.)*
4 *Write a character sketch of Ma.*
5 *Write a story about staying with relations.*
6 *One of Ma's maxims is 'Who ask don't get...'. Collect as many maxims (i.e. sayings) as you can about 'the best way to behave'. For instance, another maxim is 'Spare the rod and spoil the child'. In order to collect a good range you will have to ask other members of the family, friends, and so on. Arrange them in any order you like (for example, Most Sensible – Least Sensible) and present them to the class.*
7 *Ma 'was equal to all the vagaries of childhood. Nothing took her by surprise.' Describe as fully as possible one of your own grandparents or an elderly, energetic person whom you know.*
8 *'The Happiest Times'. (a) Write about two paragraphs describing your happiest times. (b) Interview anyone you know and ask about his or her happiest times (it could be an older person, or a member of your family, or neighbour) and write up your interview. (This may involve selecting bits of what the person says, not putting it down word for word. You may want to choose particularly interesting or vividly told bits.)*
9 *'... as if we would always be wiry-limbed children whose darting about the sun would capture like amber and fix into eternity.' Write a poem on the theme of childhood and happiness – and time standing still.*

FURTHER READING

Crick Crack Monkey Merle Hodge (Heinemann Educational Books)
Green Days by the River Michael Anthony (Heinemann Educational Books)
Christopher Geoffrey Drayton (Heinemann Educational Books)
Black Shack Alley Joseph Zobel (Heinemann Educational Books)

ANITA DESAI

Anita Desai was born in 1937. Her father was Bengali and her mother German. She was educated in Delhi and now lives in Bombay. She has been writing since the age of seven and has written novels, short stories and children's fiction. She has said of her own work: 'My novels are no reflection of Indian society, politics and character. They are part of my private effort to seize upon the raw material of life and its shapelessness, its meaninglessness . . . and to mould it and impose on it a design, a certain composition and order that pleases me as an artist and also as a human being who longs for order.'

GAMES AT TWILIGHT

It was still too hot to play outdoors. They had had their tea, they had been washed and had their hair brushed, and after the long day of confinement in the house that was not cool but at least a protection from the sun, the children strained to get out. Their faces were red and bloated with the effort, but their mother would not open the door, everything was still curtained and shuttered in a way that stifled the children, made them feel that their lungs were stuffed with cotton wool and their noses with dust and if they didn't burst out into the light and see the sun and feel the air, they would choke.

'Please, Ma, please,' they begged. 'We'll play in the veranda and porch – we won't go a step out of the porch.'

'You will, I know you will, and then—'

'No – we won't, we won't,' they wailed so horrendously that she actually let down the bolt of the front door so that they burst out like seeds from a crackling over-ripe pod into the veranda, with such wild, maniacal yells that she retreated to her bath and the shower of talcum powder and the fresh sari that were to help her face the summer evening.

They faced the afternoon. It was too hot. Too bright. The white walls of the veranda glared stridently in the sun. The bougainvillaea[1] hung about it, purple and magenta, in livid balloons. The garden outside was like a tray made of beaten brass, flattened out on the red gravel and the stony soil in all shades of metal – aluminium, tin, copper and brass. No life stirred at this arid time of day – the birds still drooped, like dead fruit, in the papery tents of the trees; some squirrels lay limp on the wet earth under the garden tap. The outdoor dog lay stretched as if dead on the veranda mat, his paws and ears and tail all reaching out like dying travellers in search of water. He rolled his eyes at the children – two white marbles rolling in the purple sockets, begging for sympathy – and attempted to lift his tail in a wag but could not. It only twitched and lay still.

Then, perhaps roused by the shrieks of the children, a band of parrots suddenly fell out of the eucalyptus tree, tumbled frantically in the still, sizzling air, then sorted themselves out into battle formation and streaked away across the white sky.

The children, too, felt released. They too began tumbling, shoving, pushing against each other, frantic to start. Start what? Start their business. The business of the children's day which is – play.

'Let's play hide-and-seek.'

'Who'll be It?'

'You be It.'

'Why should I? You be—'

'You're the eldest—'

'That doesn't mean—'

The shoves became harder. Some kicked out. The motherly Mira inter-
vened. She pulled the boys roughly apart. There was a tearing sound of cloth
but it was lost in the heavy panting and angry grumbling and no one paid
attention to the small sleeve hanging loosely off a shoulder.

'Make a circle, make a circle!' she shouted, firmly pulling and pushing till a
kind of vague circle was formed. 'Now clap!' she roared and, clapping, they all
chanted in melancholy unison: 'Dip, dip, dip – my blue ship' – and every now
and then one or the other saw he was safe by the way his hands fell at the
crucial moment – palm on palm, or back of hand on palm – and dropped out of
the circle with a yell and a jump of relief and jubilation.

Raghu was It. He started to protest, to cry 'You cheated – Mira cheated –

Anu cheated' – but it was too late, the others had all already streaked away. There was no one to hear when he called out, 'Only in the veranda – the porch – Ma said – Ma *said* to stay in the porch!' No one had stopped to listen, all he saw were their brown legs flashing through the dusty shrubs, scrambling up brick walls, leaping over compost heaps and hedges, and then the porch stood empty in the purple shade of the bougainvillaea and the garden was as empty as before; even the limp squirrels had whisked away, leaving everything gleaming, brassy and bare.

Only small Manu suddenly reappeared, as if he had dropped out of an invisible cloud or from a bird's claws, and stood for a moment in the centre of the yellow lawn, chewing his finger and near to tears as he heard Raghu shouting, with his head pressed against the veranda wall, 'Eighty-three, eighty-five, eighty-nine, ninety . . .' and then made off in a panic, half of him wanting to fly north, the other half counselling south. Raghu turned just in time to see the flash of his white shorts and the uncertain skittering of his red sandals, and charged after him with such a blood-curdling yell that Manu stumbled over the hosepipe, fell into its rubber coils and lay there weeping, 'I won't be It – you have to find them all – all – All!'

'I know I have to, idiot,' Raghu said, superciliously kicking him with his toe. 'You're dead,' he said with satisfaction, licking the beads of perspiration off his upper lip, and then stalked off in search of worthier prey, whistling spiritedly so that the hiders should hear and tremble.

Ravi heard the whistling and picked his nose in a panic, trying to find comfort by burrowing the finger deep-deep into that soft tunnel. He felt himself too exposed, sitting on an upturned flower pot behind the garage. Where could he burrow? He could run around the garage if he heard Raghu come – around and around and around – but he hadn't much faith in his short legs when matched against Raghu's long, hefty, hairy footballer legs. Ravi had a frightening glimpse of them as Raghu combed the hedge of crotons[2] and hibiscus,[3] trampling delicate ferns underfoot as he did so. Ravi looked about him desperately, swallowing a small ball of snot in his fear.

The garage was locked with a great heavy lock to which the driver had the key in his room, hanging from a nail on the wall under his work-shirt. Ravi had peeped in and seen him still sprawling on his string-cot in his vest and striped underpants, the hair on his chest and the hair in his nose shaking with the vibrations of his phlegm-obstructed snores. Ravi had wished he were tall enough, big enough to reach the key on the nail, but it was impossible, beyond his reach for years to come. He had sidled away and sat dejectedly on the flower pot. That at least was cut to his own size.

But next to the garage was another shed with a big green door. Also locked. No one even knew who had the key to the lock. That shed wasn't opened more than once a year when Ma turned out all the old broken bits of furniture and rolls of matting and leaking buckets, and the white ant hills were broken and swept away and Flit[4] sprayed into the spider webs and rat holes so that the whole operation was like the looting of a poor, ruined and conquered city. The green leaves of the door sagged. They were nearly off their rusty hinges. The hinges were large and made a small gap between the door and the walls – only just large enough for rats, dogs and, possibly, Ravi to slip through.

Ravi had never cared to enter such a dark and depressing mortuary of defunct household goods seething with such unspeakable and alarming animal life but, as Raghu's whistling grew angrier and sharper and his crashing and storming in the hedge wilder, Ravi suddenly slipped off the flower pot and through the crack and was gone. He chuckled aloud with astonishment at his own temerity so that Raghu came out of the hedge, stood silent with his hands on his hips, listening, and finally shouted 'I heard you! I'm coming! *Got* you' – and came charging round the garage only to find the upturned flower pot, the yellow dust, the crawling of white ants in a mud-hill against the closed shed door – nothing. Snarling, he bent to pick up a stick and went off, whacking it against the garage and shed walls as if to beat out his prey.

Ravi shook, then shivered with delight, with self-congratulation. Also with fear. It was dark, spooky in the shed. It had a muffled smell, as of graves. Ravi had once got locked into the linen cupboard and sat there weeping for half an hour before he was rescued. But at least that had been a familiar place, and even smelt pleasantly of starch, laundry and, reassuringly, of his mother. But the shed smelt of rats, ant hills, dust and spider webs. Also of less definable, less recognizable horrors. And it was dark. Except for the white-hot cracks along the door, there was no light. The roof was very low. Although Ravi was small, he felt as if he could reach up and touch it with his finger tips. But he didn't stretch. He hunched himself into a ball so as not to bump into anything, touch or feel anything. What might there not be to touch him and feel him as he stood there, trying to see in the dark? Something cold, or slimy – like a snake. Snakes! He leapt up as Raghu whacked the wall with his stick – then, quickly realizing what it was, felt almost relieved to hear Raghu, hear his stick. It made him feel protected.

But Raghu soon moved away. There wasn't a sound once his footsteps had gone around the garage and disappeared. Ravi stood frozen inside the shed. Then he shivered all over. Something had tickled the back of his neck. It took him a while to pick up the courage to lift his hand and explore. It was an insect – perhaps a spider – exploring *him*. He squashed it and wondered how many more creatures were watching him, waiting to reach out and touch him, the stranger.

There was nothing now. After standing in that position – his hand still on his neck, feeling the wet splodge of the squashed spider gradually dry – for minutes, hours, his legs began to tremble with the effort, the inaction. By now he could see enough in the dark to make out the large solid shapes of old wardrobes, broken buckets and bedsteads piled on top of each other around him. He recognized an old bathtub – patches of enamel glimmered at him and at last he lowered himself on to its edge.

He contemplated slipping out of the shed and into the fray. He wondered if it would not be better to be captured by Raghu and be returned to the milling crowd as long as he could be in the sun, the light, the free spaces of the garden and the familiarity of his brothers, sisters and cousins. It would be evening soon. Their games would become legitimate. The parents would sit out on the lawn on cane basket chairs and watch them as they tore around the garden or gathered in knots to share a loot of mulberries or black, teeth-splitting *jamun*[5] from the garden trees. The gardener would fix the hosepipe to the water tap and water would fall lavishly through the air to the ground, soaking the dry yellow grass and the red gravel and arousing the sweet, the intoxicating scent of water on dry earth – that loveliest scent in the world. Ravi sniffed for a whiff of it. He half-rose from the bathtub, then heard the despairing scream of one of the girls as Raghu bore down upon her. There was the sound of a crash, and of rolling about in the bushes, the shrubs, then screams and accusing sobs of 'I touched the den' – 'You did not' – 'I did' – 'You liar, you did *not*' and then a fading away and silence again.

Ravi sat back on the harsh edge of the tub, deciding to hold out a bit longer. What fun if they were all found and caught – he alone left unconquered! He had never known that sensation. Nothing more wonderful had ever happened to him than being taken out by an uncle and bought a whole slab of chocolate all to himself, or being flung into the soda-man's pony cart and driven up to the gate by the friendly driver with the red beard and pointed ears. To defeat Raghu – that hirsute, hoarse-voiced football champion – and to be the winner in a circle of older, bigger, luckier children – that would be thrilling beyond imagination. He hugged his knees together and smiled to himself almost shyly at the thought of so much victory, such laurels.

There he sat smiling, knocking his heels against the bathtub, now and then getting up and going to the door to put his ear to the broad crack and listening for sounds of the game, the pursuer and the pursued, and then returning to his seat with the dogged determination of the true winner, a breaker of records, a champion.

It grew darker in the shed as the light at the door grew softer, fuzzier, turned to a kind of crumbling yellow pollen that turned to yellow fur, blue fur, grey fur. Evening. Twilight. The sound of water gushing, falling. The scent of earth receiving water, slaking its thirst in great gulps and releasing that green scent of freshness, coolness. Through the crack Ravi saw the long purple shadows of the shed and the garage lying still across the yard. Beyond that, the white walls of the house. The bougainvillaea had lost its lividity, hung in dark bundles that quaked and twittered and seethed with masses of homing sparrows. The lawn was shut off from his view. Could he hear the children's voices? It seemed to him that he could. It seemed to him that he could hear them chanting, singing, laughing. But what about the game? What had happened? Could it be over? How could it when he was still not found?

It then occurred to him that he could have slipped out long ago, dashed across the yard to the veranda and touched the 'den'. It was necessary to do that to win. He had forgotten. He had only remembered the part of hiding and trying to elude the seeker. He had done that so successfully, his success had occupied him so wholly that he had quite forgotten that success had to be clinched by that final dash to victory and the ringing cry of 'Den!'

With a whimper he burst through the crack, fell on his knees, got up and stumbled on stiff, benumbed legs across the shadowy yard, crying heartily by the time he reached the veranda so that when he flung himself at the white pillar and bawled, 'Den! Den! Den!' his voice broke with rage and pity at the disgrace of it all and he felt himself flooded with tears and misery.

Out on the lawn, the children stopped chanting. They all turned to stare at him in amazement. Their faces were pale and triangular in the dusk. The trees and bushes around them stood inky and sepulchral, spilling long shadows across them. They stared, wondering at his reappearance, his passion, his wild animal howling. Their mother rose from her basket chair and came towards him, worried, annoyed, saying, 'Stop it, stop it, Ravi. Don't be a baby. Have you hurt yourself?' Seeing him attended to, the children went back to clasping their hands and chanting 'The grass is green, the rose is red....'

But Ravi would not let them. He tore himself out of his mother's grasp and pounded across the lawn into their midst, charging at them with his head lowered so that they scattered in surprise. 'I won, I won, I won,' he bawled, shaking his head so that the big tears flew. 'Raghu didn't find me. I won, I won—'

It took them a minute to grasp what he was saying, even who he was. They had quite forgotten him. Raghu had found all the others long ago. There had been a fight about who was to be It next. It had been so fierce that their mother had emerged from her bath and made them change to another game. Then they had played another and another. Broken mulberries from the tree and eaten them. Helped the driver wash the car when their father returned from work. Helped the gardener water the beds till he roared at them and swore he would complain to their parents. The parents had come out, taken up their positions on the cane chairs. They had begun to play again, sing and chant. All this time no one had remembered Ravi. Having disappeared from the scene, he had disappeared from their minds. Clean.

'Don't be a fool,' Raghu said roughly, pushing him aside, and even Mira said, 'Stop howling, Ravi. If you want to play, you can stand at the end of the line,' and she put him there very firmly.

The game proceeded. Two pairs of arms reached up and met in an arc. The children stooped under it again and again in a lugubrious circle, ducking their heads and intoning

The grass is green,
The rose is red;
Remember me
When I am dead, dead, dead, dead . . .

And the arc of thin arms trembled in the twilight, and the heads were bowed so sadly, and their feet tramped to that melancholy refrain so mournfully, so helplessly, that Ravi could not bear it. He would not follow them, he would not be included in this funeral game. He had wanted victory and triumph – not a funeral. But he had been forgotten, left out and he would not join them now. The ignominy of being forgotten – how could he face it? He felt his heart go heavy and ache inside him unbearably. He lay down full length on the damp grass, crushing his face into it, no longer crying, silenced by a terrible sense of his insignificance.

GLOSSARY
1 *bougainvillaea*: a very decorative tropical bush with brilliant pink or purple blossoms.
2 *crotons*: a croton is a tropical plant with eye-catching multi-coloured leaves of deep red, orange, yellow and green.
3 *hibiscus*: also called 'shoe-flower'. A bush with large, striking trumpet-shaped flowers, usually red.
4 *Flit*: insect spray.
5 *jamun*: a small black fruit resembling an olive.

SUGGESTIONS FOR WRITING AND DISCUSSION

1 *How does the author manage to convey the heat of the afternoon?*
2 *As far as possible, describe the characters of the different children (Ravi, Raghu, Mira and Manu).*
3 *How would you sum up their games and behaviour?*
4 *Why was Ravi so upset?*
5 *Compare the children in this story and their way of life with those in 'Staying with Ma'.*
6 *Write a story about children playing where something goes wrong.*
7 *Several games are mentioned in the story: hide and seek, 'dip, dip, dip . . .' and 'the grass is green . . .'. Prepare a dossier of children's games known to your group. Your descriptions should be very clear as to the rules, actions involved, and so on. If any rhymes are used – as in skipping and clapping games – be sure to include them.*
8 *Read again the description of the shed 'with a big green door'. Think of a boarded-up building in your area (a closed shop, a house or row of houses waiting for repair or demolition). Then carefully describe the outside appearance and give your impression of what the inside would be like.*

FURTHER READING

Games at Twilight Anita Desai (Penguin)
Fire on the Mountain Anita Desai (Penguin)
A Village by the Sea Anita Desai (Heinemann Educational Books)

PETER ABRAHAMS

Peter Abrahams was born in 1919 in Vrededorp, a crowded slum suburb of Johannesburg. His mother was a Cape Coloured of Malay origin and his father, who died when Abrahams was very young, was an Ethiopian. Abrahams's childhood was one of great poverty and hardship. After he had left school he worked as a clerk and wrote poetry and political articles. He left South Africa in 1940 by enlisting as a seaman on a British ship. After living in England for several years, working as a newspaper and radio journalist, he went to Jamaica and since 1977 has been Chairman of Radio Jamaica.

Abrahams's early life is set out in his autobiographical novel, *Tell Freedom*. In these extracts Lee (the author) has been sent by his mother (who works for a white family and lives in) to stay with his Aunt Liza and Uncle Sam. His uncle is a farmworker for an Afrikaner family in the northern Transvaal. It is winter and the early mornings are very cold.

CRACKLING DAY

Wednesday was crackling day. On that day the children of the location[1] made the long trek to Elsburg siding for the squares of pig's rind that passed for our daily meat. We collected a double lot of cow dung[2] the day before; a double lot of *moeroga*.[3]

I finished my breakfast and washed up. Aunt Liza was at her wash-tub in the yard. A misty, sickly sun was just showing. And on the open veld[4] the frost lay thick and white on the grass.

'Ready?' Aunt Liza called.

I went out to her. She shook the soapsuds off her swollen hands and wiped them on her apron. She lifted the apron and put her hand through the slits of the many thin cotton dresses she wore. The dress nearest the skin was the one with the pocket. From this she pulled a sixpenny piece. She tied it in a knot in the corner of a bit of coloured cloth.

'Take care of that. . . . Take the smaller piece of bread in the bin but don't eat it till you start back. You can have a small piece of crackling with it. Only a small piece, understand?'

'Yes, Aunt Liza.'

'All right.'

I got the bread and tucked it into the little canvas bag in which I would carry the crackling.

''Bye, Aunt Liza.' I trotted off, one hand in my pocket, feeling the cloth where the money was. I paused at Andries's home.

'Andries!' I danced up and down while I waited. The cold was not so terrible on bare feet if one did not keep still.

Andries came trotting out of their yard. His mother's voice followed; desperate and plaintive:

'I'll skin you if you lose the money!'

'Women!' Andries said bitterly.

I glimpsed the dark, skinny woman at her wash-tub as we trotted across the veld. Behind, and in front of us, other children trotted in two's and three's.

There was a sharp bite to the morning air I sucked in; it stung my nose so that tears came to my eyes; it went down my throat like an icy draught; my nose ran. I tried breathing through my mouth but this was worse. The cold went through my shirt and shorts; my skin went pimply and chilled; my fingers went numb and began to ache; my feet felt like frozen lumps that did

not belong to me, yet jarred and hurt each time I put them down. I began to feel sick and desperate.

We went faster. We passed two children, sobbing and moaning as they ran. We were all in the same desperate situation. We were creatures haunted and hounded by the cold. It was a cruel enemy who gave no quarter. And our means of fighting it were pitifully inadequate. In all the mornings and evenings of the winter months, young and old, big and small were helpless victims of the bitter cold. Only towards noon and the early afternoon, when the sun sat high in the sky, was there a brief respite. For us, the children, the cold, especially the morning cold, assumed an awful and malevolent personality. We talked of 'It'. 'It' was a half-human monster with evil thoughts, evil intentions, bent on destroying us. 'It' was happiest when we were most miserable. Andries had told me how 'It' had, last winter, caught and killed a boy.

Hunger was an enemy too, but one with whom we could come to terms, who had many virtues and values. Hunger gave our *pap*,[5] *moeroga* and crackling a feast-like quality. We could, when it was not with us, think and talk kindly about it. Its memory could even give moments of laughter. But the cold of winter was with us all the time. 'It' never really eased up. There were only more bearable degrees of 'It' at high noon and on mild days. 'It' was the real enemy. And on this Wednesday morning, as we ran across the veld, winter was more bitterly, bitingly, freezingly, real than ever.

The sun climbed. The frozen earth thawed, leaving the short grass looking wet and weary. Painfully, our feet and legs came alive. The aching numbness slowly left our fingers. We ran more slowly in the more bearable cold.

In climbing, the sun lost some of its damp look and seemed a real, if cold, sun. When it was right overhead, we struck the sandy road which meant we were nearing the siding. None of the others were in sight. Andries and I were alone on the sandy road on the open veld. We slowed down to a brisk walk. We were sufficiently thawed to want to talk.

'How far?' I said.

'A few minutes,' he said.

'I've got a piece of bread,' I said.

'Me too,' he said. 'Let's eat it now.'

'On the way back,' I said. 'With a bit of crackling.'

'Good idea. . . . Race to the fork.'

'All right.'

'Go!' he said.

We shot off together, legs working like pistons. He soon pulled away from me. He reached the fork in the road some fifty yards ahead.

'I win!' he shouted gleefully, though his teeth still chattered.

We pitched stones down the road, each trying to pitch further than the other. I won and wanted to go on doing it. But Andries soon grew weary with pitching. We raced again. Again he won. He wanted another race but I refused. I wanted pitching, but he refused. So, sulking with each other, we reached the pig farm.

We followed a fenced-off pathway round sprawling white buildings. Everywhere about us was the grunt of pigs. As we passed an open doorway, a huge dog came bounding out, snarling and barking at us. In our terror, we forgot it was fenced in and streaked away. Surprised, I found myself a good distance ahead of Andries. We looked back and saw a young white woman call the dog to heel.

'Damn Boer dog,' Andries said.

'Matter with it?' I asked.

'They teach them to go for us. Never get caught by one.'

I remembered I had outstripped him.

'I won!' I said.

'Only because you were frightened,' he said.

'I'll knock you!'

'I'll knock you back!'

A couple of white men came down the path and ended our possible fight. We hurried past them to the distant shed where a queue had already formed. There were grown-ups and children. All the grown-ups, and some of the children, were from places other than our location.

The line moved slowly. The young white man who served us did it in leisurely fashion, with long pauses for a smoke. Occasionally he turned his back.

At last, after what seemed hours, my turn came. Andries was behind me. I took the sixpenny piece from the square of cloth and offered it to the man.

'Well?' he said.

'Sixpence crackling, please.'

Andries nudged me in the back. The man's stare suddenly became cold and hard. Andries whispered into my ear.

'Well?' the man repeated coldly.

'Please, *baas*,'[6] I said.

'What d'you want?'

'Sixpence crackling, please.'

'What?'

Andries dug me in the ribs.

'Sixpence crackling, please, *baas*.'

'What?'

'Sixpence crackling, please, *baas*.'

'You new here?'

'Yes, *baas*.' I looked at his feet while he stared at me.

At last he took the sixpenny piece from me. I held my bag open while he filled it with crackling from a huge pile on a large canvas sheet on the ground. Turning away, I stole a fleeting glance at his face. His eyes met mine, and there was amused, challenging mockery in them. I waited for Andries at the back of the queue, out of the reach of the white man's mocking eyes.

The cold day was at its mildest as we walked home along the sandy road. I took out my piece of bread and, with a small piece of greasy crackling, still warm, on it, I munched as we went along. We had not yet made our peace so Andries munched his bread and crackling on the other side of the road.

Thus, we reached the fork. Andries saw them first and moved over to my side of the road.

'White boys,' he said.

There were three of them. Two of about our own size and one slightly bigger. They had school bags and were coming towards us up the road from the siding.

'Better run for it,' Andries said.

'Why?'

'No, that'll draw them. Let's just walk along, but quickly.'

'Why?' I repeated.

'Shut up,' he said.

Some of his anxiety touched me. Our own scrap was forgotten. We marched side by side as fast as we could. The white boys saw us and hurried up the road. We passed the fork. Perhaps they would take the turning away from us. We dared not look back.

'Hear them?' Andries asked.

'No.'

I looked over my shoulder.

'They're coming,' I said.

'Walk faster,' Andries said. 'If they come closer, run.'

'Hey, *klipkop*!'[7]

'Don't look back,' Andries said.

'Hottentot!'

We walked as fast as we could.

Ahead was a bend in the road. Behind the bend were bushes. Once there, we could run without them knowing it till it was too late.

'Faster,' Andries said.

They began pelting us with stones.

'Run when we get to the bushes,' Andries said.

The bend and the bushes were near. We would soon be there.

A clear young voice carried to us:

'Your fathers are dirty black baboons!'

'Run!' Andries called.

A violent, unreasoning anger suddenly possessed me. I stopped and turned.

'You're a liar!' I screamed it.

The foremost boy pointed at me:

'An ugly black baboon!'

In a fog of rage I went towards him.

'Liar!' I shouted. 'My father was better than your father!'

I neared them. The bigger boy stepped between me and the one I was after.

'My father was better than your father! Liar!'

The big boy struck me a mighty clout on the side of the face. I staggered, righted myself, and leapt at the boy who had insulted my father. I struck him on the face, hard. A heavy blow on the back of my head nearly stunned me. I grabbed at the boy in front of me. We went down together.

'Liar!' I said through clenched teeth, hitting him with all my might.

Blows rained on me, on my head, my neck, the side of my face, my mouth, but my enemy was under me and I pounded him fiercely, all the time repeating:

'Liar! Liar! Liar!'

Suddenly, stars exploded in my head. Then there was darkness.

I emerged from the darkness to find Andries kneeling beside me.

'God, man! I thought they'd killed you.'

I sat up. The white boys were nowhere to be seen. Like Andries, they'd probably thought me dead and run off in panic. The inside of my mouth felt sore and swollen. My nose was tender to the touch. The back of my head ached. A trickle of blood dripped from my nose. I stemmed it with the square of coloured cloth. The greatest damage was to my shirt. It was ripped in many places. I remembered the crackling. I looked anxiously about. It was safe, a little off the road on the grass. I relaxed. I got up and brushed my clothes. I picked up the crackling.

'God, you're dumb!' Andries said. 'You're going to get it!'

I was too depressed to retort. Besides, I knew he was right. I was dumb. I should have run when he told me to.

'Come on,' I said.

One of many small groups of children, each child carrying his little bag of crackling, we trod the long road home in the cold winter afternoon.

There was tension in the house that night. When I got back Aunt Liza had listened to the story in silence. The beating or scolding I expected did not come. But Aunt Liza changed while she listened, became remote and withdrawn. When Uncle Sam came home she told him what had happened. He, too, just looked at me and became more remote and withdrawn than usual. They were waiting for something; their tension reached out to me, and I waited with them, anxious, apprehensive.

The thing we waited for came while we were having our supper. We heard a trap pull up outside.

'Here it is,' Uncle Sam said and got up.

Aunt Liza leaned back from the table and put her hands in her lap, fingers intertwined, a cold, unseeing look in her eyes.

Before Uncle Sam reached it, the door burst open. A tall, broad, white man strode in. Behind him came the three boys. The one I had attacked had swollen lips and a puffy left eye.

'Evening, *baas*,' Uncle Sam murmured.

'That's him,' the bigger boy said, pointing at me.

The white man stared till I lowered my eyes.

'Well?' he said.

'He's sorry, *baas*,' Uncle Sam said quickly. 'I've given him a hiding he won't forget soon. You know how it is, *baas*. He's new here, the child of a relative in Johannesburg and they don't all know how to behave there. You know how it is in the big towns, *baas*.' The plea in Uncle Sam's voice had grown more pronounced as he went on. He turned to me. 'Tell the *baas* and *basies* how sorry you are, Lee.'

I looked at Aunt Liza and something in her lifelessness made me stubborn in spite of my fear.

'He insulted my father,' I said.

The white man smiled.

'See, Sam, your hiding couldn't have been good.'

There was a flicker of life in Aunt Liza's eyes. For a brief moment she saw me, looked at me, warmly, lovingly, then her eyes went dead again.

'He's only a child, *baas*,' Uncle Sam murmured.

'You stubborn too, Sam?'

'No, *baas*.'

'Good. ... Then teach him, Sam. If you and he are to live here, you must teach him. Well...?'

'Yes, *baas*.'

Uncle Sam went into the other room and returned with a thick leather thong. He wound it once round his hand and advanced on me. The man and boys leaned against the door, watching. I looked at Aunt Liza's face. Though there was no sign of life or feeling on it, I knew suddenly, instinctively, that she wanted me not to cry.

Bitterly, Uncle Sam said:

'You must never lift your hand to a white person. No matter what happens, you must never lift your hand to a white person....'

He lifted the strap and brought it down on my back. I clenched my teeth and stared at Aunt Liza. I did not cry with the first three strokes. Then, suddenly, Aunt Liza went limp. Tears showed in her eyes. The thong came down on my back, again and again. I screamed and begged for mercy. I grovelled at Uncle Sam's feet, begging him to stop, promising never to lift my hand to any white person....

At last, the white man's voice said:

'All right, Sam.'

Uncle Sam stopped. I lay whimpering on the floor. Aunt Liza sat like one in a trance.

'Is he still stubborn, Sam?'

'Tell the *baas* and *basies* you are sorry.'

'I'm sorry,' I said.

'Bet his father is one of those who believe in equality.'

'His father is dead,' Aunt Liza said.

'Good night, Sam.'

'Good night, *baas*. Sorry about this.'

'All right, Sam.' He opened the door. The boys went out first, then he followed. 'Good night, Liza.'

Aunt Liza did not answer. The door shut behind the white folk, and, soon, we heard their trap moving away. Uncle Sam flung the thong viciously against the door, slumped down on the bench, folded his arms on the table, and buried his head on his arms. Aunt Liza moved away from him, came on the floor beside me and lifted me into her large lap. She sat rocking my body. Uncle Sam began to sob softly. After some time, he raised his head and looked at us.

'Explain to the child, Liza,' he said.

'You explain,' Aunt Liza said bitterly. 'You are the man. You did the beating. You are the head of the family. This is a man's world. You do the explaining.'

'Please, Liza....'

'You should be happy. The whites are satisfied. We can go on now.'

With me in her arms, Aunt Liza got up. She carried me into the other room. The food on the table remained half-eaten. She laid me on the bed on my stomach, smeared fat on my back, then covered me with the blankets. She undressed and got into bed beside me. She cuddled me close, warmed me with her own body. With her big hand on my cheek, she rocked me, first to silence, then to sleep.

For the only time of my stay there, I slept on a bed in Elsburg.

When I woke next morning Uncle Sam had gone. Aunt Liza only once referred to the beating he had given me. It was in the late afternoon, when I returned with the day's cow dung.

'It hurt him,' she said. 'You'll understand one day.'

That night, Uncle Sam brought me an orange, a bag of boiled sweets, and a dirty old picture book. He smiled as he gave them to me, rather anxiously. When I smiled back at him, he seemed to relax. He put his hand on my head, started to say something, then changed his mind and took his seat by the fire.

Aunt Liza looked up from the floor where she dished out the food.

'It's all right, old man,' she murmured.

'One day ...,' Uncle Sam said.

'It's all right,' Aunt Liza repeated insistently.

GLOSSARY

1 *the location*: area where black South Africans living in urban areas are obliged to live in South Africa. Now also known as 'townships'.
2 *cow dung*: dried cow dung was used as a fuel for fires.
3 *moeroga*: wild spinach.
4 *veld*: open country (Afrikaans = field).
5 *pap*: a porridge made of crushed maize boiled in salted water.
6 *baas*: master (Afrikaans).
7 *klipkop*: rockhead (Afrikaans insult).

SUGGESTIONS FOR WRITING AND DISCUSSION

1 *How does the author manage to convey the coldness of the winters? Why did the narrator (Lee) and the others feel its effects particularly?*
2 *Comment on the attitude of the white man serving out the crackling.*
3 *What are your reactions to the fight between Lee and the three white boys?*

4 *Describe and comment on what you learn about the attitudes and feelings of Aunt Liza and Uncle Sam towards the white man and the beating.*
5 *What do you think about the way whites and blacks behave in this extract?*
6 *Write a story about a child being punished unjustly.*
7 *Write a short case study on apartheid in South Africa. Compare the situation today with that in the late 1920s (when the narrator would have been about ten years old). You could consider the following points: the franchise and right to vote; schooling for people of the different races; work opportunities; the pass laws; regulations relating to mixed marriages; opposition to apartheid then and now.*
8 *Write a short report on the relations between people of different races in your area. You could include your own ideas and things you have noticed, the remarks of others (of various races), and the results of a few short interviews with set questions. This could be presented to the rest of the class as a group report.*
9 *You have been asked to join a team that is preparing a programme to help combat racism and prejudice in a British town. Work out a six-point programme to put forward at the next team meeting. Be prepared to argue your case as eloquently and as convincingly as you can.*

LEE, COLOURED

'Aunt Liza. . . .'
'Yes?'
'What am I?'
'What are you talking about?'
'I met a boy at the river. He said he was Zulu.'
She laughed.
'You are Coloured.[1] There are three kinds of people: white people, Coloured people, and black people. The white people come first, then the Coloured people, then the black people.'
'Why?'
'Because it is so.'
Next day, when I met Joseph, I smacked my chest and said:
'Lee! Coloured!'
He clapped his hands and laughed.

Joseph and I spent most of the long summer afternoons together. He learnt some Afrikaans[2] from me; I learnt some Zulu from him. Our days were full.
There was the river to explore.
There were my swimming lessons, and others.
I learnt to fight with sticks; to weave a green hat of young willow wands and leaves; to catch frogs and tadpoles with my hands; to set a trap for the

springhaas;[3] to make the sounds of the river birds.

There was the hot sun to comfort us. . . .

There was the green grass to dry our bodies. . . .

There was the soft clay with which to build. . . .

There was the fine sand with which to fight. . . .

There were our giant grasshoppers to race. . . .

There were the locust swarms when the skies turned black and we caught them by the hundreds. . . .

There was the rare taste of crisp, brown baked, salted locusts. . . .

There was the voice of the wind in the willows. . . .

There was the voice of the heaven in thunderstorms. . . .

There were the voices of two children in laughter, ours. . . .

There were Joseph's tales of black kings who lived in days before the white man. . . .

At home, I said:

'Aunt Liza . . .'

'Yes?'

'Did we have Coloured kings before the white man?'

'No.'

'Then where did we come from? Joseph and his mother come from the black kings who were before the white man.'

And laughing, and ruffling my head, she said:

'You talk too much . . . Go'n wash up.'

GLOSSARY

1 *Coloured*: an official term used in South Africa to describe people of mixed racial descent.
2 *Afrikaans*: one of the languages spoken as a mother tongue in South Africa. It originates from Dutch.
3 *springhaas*: hare (Afrikaans).

SUGGESTIONS FOR WRITING AND DISCUSSION

1 What do you learn from this extract about life in South Africa?
2 What do you think the writer's views on race are?
3 Describe the style in which this extract is written and comment on its effectiveness.
4 Can you justify saying that this extract is a kind of poem?
5 Prepare this extract as a dramatized reading with different voices. Try recording a final version.

FURTHER READING

Tell Freedom Peter Abrahams (Faber)
Mine Boy Peter Abrahams (Heinemann Educational Books)
A Wreath for Udomo Peter Abrahams (Faber)

IAN MCDONALD

Ian McDonald was born in
Trinidad in 1933, and educated
in Port of Spain and at
Cambridge University where he
read history. His poetry has
appeared in a number of
anthologies of Caribbean poetry
and he has written a play,
Tramping Men, which was
produced by the Guyana
Theatre Guild in 1969. He now
lives in Guyana and is a director
of one of the country's large
sugar companies.

The Humming-Bird Tree
describes the friendship of a rich
white Trinidadian boy with his
family's East Indian yard-boy,
Kaiser, and his love for Kaiser's
sister Jaillin which is doomed to
end tragically because of
differences in race and class.

THE MARBLEUS

The scent of hog plums lay in the ground. Their fragrance was sweet and subtle and a person who didn't know better would have thought for sure that each one of the deep orange plums scattered under the river trees must prove a delicious, juicy thing in the mouth, fruit as good any day as a mango or a rich purple governor plum. Yet only bats would eat them, they were so acid. I remember once Kaiser fooled me. It was my first adventure up the river with him. He had picked one of the plums up and offered me it.

'Man, tas'e dat if you really want to know what fruit tas'e like.'

I bit into the plum, for it smelled as sweet even as sugared cherries, the kind we bought in the tall glass bottles and which the servants used to put in gin-and-orange drinks when friends visited. I actually shuddered with the shock; the acid juice set my body on edge. I spat and spat on the ground and looked fiercely at Kaiser.

'Ha! Ha! Boy, I bet you never tas'e fruit like that before! What you is at all, a bat or what?'

'That's not funny. Perhaps it's poisonous.'

Kaiser laughed again. Ever since that time I had wanted to play the same trick on some other innocent who didn't know about hog plums and important things like that. But I never got the chance.

At that moment, I was not thinking about hog plums. In front of me lay a treasure so great that my eyes dazzled in the sight of it. Not more than two yards away two marbleus were settled on the wet black rock. These are the rarest butterflies and for a boy they were worth more than toy soldiers (like those I had with miniature black busbies on at home), an electric train or bow and arrow, even more than the pirate gold I hoped to find one day in the garden. And they were so close that my net on the long bamboo pole would easily reach them with one wide swoop. I noticed they were stuck together at the ends of their thin brown bodies and I couldn't understand this. But it didn't matter, the main thing was that the posture made them so easy to catch. I had never seen a marbleu settled before. Generally they flew high and fast down the middle of the river and so were impossible to catch. Only one of my friends had a specimen, and that was old and battered; we teased him that his grandfather had given it to him, that it was out of date. Now two of them had settled clumsily on an open rock face, like a special sacrifice to me. Their deep blue wings lay against the black stone, like fragments of linen tacked on to black sugarcloth. I knelt watching them, in one of boyhood's trances. Sometimes their wings moved lazily upwards and gently down, as if a delicate wind disturbed them; then the little light there was under the trees gathered in the wings and they shone in my eyes like triangles of blue glass reflecting a cloudless sun. It was the most beautiful thing I ever saw.

I knelt forward, almost in worship. But as I raised the bamboo pole ever so carefully, slowly (if I had done it quickly, with vehemence, I think I would have caught them), my knee slipped on the wet rock and my hands went sprawling, with the net, to save myself. The marbleus were disturbed by this gross fall and carefully, still together, they lifted themselves off the rock and flew down over the river where it rushed white and dangerous between the black rock walls.

Their blue wings moved languidly as they dipped and floated away from me. I recovered quickly and, standing up, made wide and desperate sweeps at them as far as my reach went over the edge of the rock. I had tears in my eyes, and as it became plain that they were escaped for good it suddenly came to me that nothing crueller might ever happen to me in life. The hurt struck me into marble stillness on the edge of black rock. I stood as if I would never move again unless it was to hurl myself in a fury of frustration into the sharp-rocked tiger water raging beneath me. I had left my large poison bottle under the leaves of a tough mountain lily growing higher up the rock where it held a little earth, and now I fetched it down (it contained a coffee, a lady slipper and two donkey eyes) and flung it into the river. That gave me some satisfaction and I stood less hurt then.

I didn't stand there for long. I heard a shout from lower down the river: 'Hey, man! Come and see what I get!'

I went down to where Kaiser was squatting on a fat stone. He looked pleased with himself. A few minutes before I had left him chasing a king-fisher butterfly hell for leather. I saw he had caught it. The kingfisher had a thick, unlovely body and big eyes like beads. I think it must have been a sort of moth, and not a real butterfly. Anyway, its wings were truly beautiful, glossy brown, fringed delicately with purple, and in the centre of each a star of scarlet. It was almost as good a catch as the marbleus would have been.

'You know already how fast these things does fly, eh, boy? Well, he settle just one time on a lily leaf back there and pap! I pick he off like a bird, man!'

He grinned and flung his hair backwards.

The butterfly lay dead in his poison bottle, resting on the white camphor. I could see that Kaiser had crushed its head between his fingers to make quite sure of his catch. He was smiling so that it hurt to think of the marbleus I had lost.

'I tell you, you know, Kaiser, I nearly caught two marbleus just now.'

'You only boas'ing. You is jealous, man. What you jealous for? I is giving this one here to you for keeps anyhow.'

If there had been nothing else I would have accepted joyfully – an offer like that wasn't to be expected every day – but now I was intent only on convinc-ing him that what I had said about the marbleus was true.

'But I'm telling you, really, Kaiser. They were joined together and almost as if they were asleep there on the rock, just up there.' Out of desperation I was much more convincing.

'Join together! But, man, what you telling me! You don't know yet that you mus' never whatever you do in this worl' try catch two but'flies who join up like that. You well lucky, man. You well escape. You don't know if you had catch them you would ha' pee your bed all nex' week and maybe worse things than that even. Talk 'bout ghosts haunting; man, those marble us'd've haunt you' backside off for you. You well lucky.'

This dark knowledge surprised me. I now thought myself rather as sweet in the eyes of God than cursed by a demon of ill-luck. What good fortune not to have caught them! Another thing puzzled me though.

'But why were they joined together at all?'

'You mean you don't know why! You really green as grass, boy. You' Mam and Pap join up jus' so when they making you, boy, the same way as dem but'flies. It's the same t'ing they was doing.' He paused, appreciating my innocence.

'But don't worry your head 'bout those things,' Kaiser went on with a dismissing gesture. 'They is only grow-up people business. You don't have to bother wid that at all. As Ol' Boss up in the village say, "ignorance does live dam' happy!"'

'But why should I be ignorant? It's something to do with love, isn't it? I've read some books, you know.'

'What books know 'bout that, eh? But don't bother your head at all, boy.'

It was coming on to rain. It was getting darker than ever under the trees that leaned over the black rocks. The roar of the river came to our ears ominously like thunder now. A small wind breathed in the branches over our heads. It was prophesying a sudden lash of rain, I was sure.

'Where d'you think we could shelter, Kaiser? It's going to rain.'

He must have known the rain was coming but he hadn't moved an inch. He had a peeled tamarind[1] stick in his hand and with it he dug at the hard earth as he sat forwards, forearms on knees, on the fat stone. His butterflying pole lay beside him. Its mosquito-netting bag was coloured red. He had told me that butterflies couldn't see red very well, but I had not yet got my mother to dye my net that efficacious colour and the white heap of it lay in contrast a few yards away. Now Kaiser grunted a little sourly.

'You all right, man. I don't min' a dam' if I get soak right through in the dam' rain. It only because you got a nice shirt that you want to run and hide from a little bit o' water. I could be a fish here. I don't mind one dam'.'

I looked at the thin tropical shirt I was wearing. It was made of a fine blue poplin material. I had rolled the sleeves up past my elbows untidily, the tails had long ago crept out of the khaki pants I wore, but despite its dishevelment anybody could see it was a good shirt.

Kaiser wasn't wearing a shirt. The only clothing he had on was a pair of khaki pants, like mine but much shorter (and the legs were different lengths), much more tattered and torn, much dirtier. It was belted with a piece of yellow string. I envied him.

'Oh, I don't mind getting wet. Once down the Islands I stayed out in the rain and got wet. It was much wetter than just having a bath. It smelled better too. Mother was vexed though. You might catch pneumonia, that's the thing. You spell it with a pee.'

'Ha! Ha! Boy, how you could spell it with a pee!'

'Oh, blast, Kaiser, you know I didn't mean that.'

'Anyhow, boy, you know what; you too soft.'

'All right then, I'll just go and put my shirt away, then you'll see. Who's afraid of rain?'

I scrambled up the rock, pulled off my shirt, rolled it up carelessly, and put it in a hollow trunk of immortelle[2] where it was almost dry. Then I slid back down, smiling, gay, and said:

'I don't mind a dam' about the rain now!' Suddenly I felt such freedom. The bones in me were looser. My body surged with confidence. Joy abounded in me. I felt I could do anything in this new, exciting, uncomplicated world. I leaped around Kaiser exclaiming. Again and again I shouted:

'I don't care one dam', see!'

Kaiser grinned up at me. He flicked some earth over my legs with his tamarind stick.

'You is a hero, boy!'

When the rain did come we stayed there and danced in it. It began with a scattering of huge drops that cracked like bullets on the leaves overhead and on the rock.

If one hit you it stung hard. Then a stillness in which we hardly dared to draw a breath. Hush. The rain streamed down and the world was wet, the earth soggy, in a minute. It ran over the black rock so that it glistened like a cape. The rain poured on us as if we were under buckets and we laughed and laughed. I closed my eyes and tilted up my face to the rain. I opened my mouth and drank the rain; I thought it tasted like blood, blood from the sky; perhaps it was dripping from hurt flamingoes. We tossed our heads and the water sprayed out of our hair; we tried to fling the water into each other's face from the long, wet locks, his black as a blackbird's wing, mine fair, almost flaxen. The smell of rain new on the baked ground, in it the fragrance of fresh nutbread, of salmon pools, of green-fern roots dug out of the ground, seemed to make us drunk. We leaped like monkeys around a hoard of bananas.

'We is fish!' Kaiser shouted. 'We is fish! We don't give a dam', we don't give a blast, we don't give a fuck!'

I repeated what he said, delirious with the joy of rain. We shouted and laughed and danced about. It was a wild glory of boys. We were near to each other in the joy. We touched hands and spun about in crazy waltzes. The rain pelted down and the trees groaned with the bigger wind. We vowed to be friends for ever. For sure, which of us will dance like that again?

The difference between us was that I was white and he was dark brown. That, I suppose, was the major difference. But there were other differences. He was older than I, fourteen he said, though I think he may have been more than that; I was not quite twelve. And yet I was as tall as he and my limbs and body as big as his. Not half as tough though. One of the first things he had done when I met him was ask me to feel his muscles. They were hard. When he pressed mine with his stubby, powerful fingers they gave like rubber. He laughed at me:

'You have muscle like a fairy, boy, or what!'

I did not speak to him for days after that, but secretly punched the pillows in bed at night, tested the puny and despised muscles almost every hour. If it was possible I wanted to be as strong as he was.

Kaiser was strong and hard all over. He had a heavy neck, a deep chest and his slightly bowed legs were thick with firm and bulgy calf-muscles. In comparison with him I was altogether flabby. Just to look at him I felt soft. My big bones were covered with tender, pampered flesh, and in contrast with his brown and shining skin my milky complexion seemed to proclaim a sickly weakness. Sometimes he called me White Cockroach, terrible insult! His skin was fine, smooth as silk and dark. When he ran or otherwise exerted himself it rippled evenly where the good muscles tightened and relaxed underneath.

He could run faster than I and was more active in every way. One day we ran a race from the old samaan tree[3] up the pitch road to the plum tree near the railway line. He beat me by twenty yards and I was sobbing with lack of breath when I came up to him. He then swung into the branches of one of the plum trees; he did it with all the ease and assurance in the world. Then I was not expert at the happy art of climbing trees and I watched him enviously. I got laboriously up with him, and from our perch we looked out for adventure. After a few minutes we saw old Ramlal, the village rum-dealer, coming down to fill a bucket from the water-pump further on.

'Let we pelt he. He only a dirty coolie[4] t'ief!'

'I don't think we should, you know, Kaiser. You should have respect for old people like that.'

Kaiser wasn't listening. He picked a handful of green-hard plums and pelted Ramlal as he passed. I tried to stop him but at once I saw the thrill of the game. I tossed one plum tentatively at the old man; it landed square on his thin nose! I was delighted and shocked. This was a terrifying adventure for me. I quivered at the thought of showing such disrespect to a grown-up. But Kaiser only bawled with laughter as the surprised old man looked about to see what had hit him so hard in the head. He shook his greasy hat at us, cursed us roundly.

'You dam' little boys playing your arse all the dam' time! Who you think you is? You think you is badjohns?[5] Come down here and see if I don't beat you up and down. Police should lock all you up.'

Kaiser only laughed. I felt guilty and ashamed. I stopped throwing the plums.

'And as for you, Master Alan, what happen to you at all, pelt'ng a old man who only minding he own business. I bet I tell your mam here today and she lick your backside off for you!'

He went off, mumbling angrily and clanking his bucket. His last threat had sobered even Kaiser, though in defiance he stubbornly continued to force a laugh until the old man was out of earshot. He knew that any complaint about us getting back to my parents would mean his dismissal. He was certainly afraid of that. He had then been with us only a few weeks.

Kaiser was the family yard-boy. He cut the lawn, kept the flower beds tidy, looked after the fowls and ducks, tended the fruit trees, cleaned and polished the car (that was the work he liked). He did all sorts of odd jobs about the house, cleaning the shoes and washing floors, killing chickens for lunch, polishing the silverware, picking lemons for Alice, the cook. The spare time he had he played with me. We had become good friends from the start. I was shy, I did not make friends easily, but with him I felt contented.

A few weeks before my father had taken him on for the job. He was very conscientious and I could never tempt him to come and play when he was engaged in some work for my mother. I remember hearing her say that she had never known a better yard-boy, one that worked harder. My father had said something about a new broom sweeping clean, but he too said that Kaiser worked hard enough, and soon he trusted him with more and more important jobs. Kaiser badly wanted to keep the position. He was getting better pay than he would get anywhere else as well as food and often, if he was lucky, some of the old clothes I had discarded and the tennis shoes that had holes in them. Kaiser played a big part in supporting his family. They lived in the village, cramped into a small mud hut. One of that family was his sister, Jaillin, a young girl who also worked for us in the house. She and Kaiser were good friends and so we three were together often. She had come with us today butterflying but had left us long before, even before we had got to the dark river where the excitement of chasing began. She had said something about going to see Mother Gawmy, an old woman who cooked bakes for sale and lived near where the path up the hill ended.

I never thought of domineering it over Kaiser, though at first I sometimes took pleasure at home in ordering him to clean my shoes, sharpen my boy scout's knife on the whetstone so that it shone, clean the bicycle I owned. He never disobeyed me, or made any comment at all, in the course of his work, and it gave me a feeling of power. But as time went on I took less and less advantage of my position as master in relation to him. It didn't seem much fun any more.

The truth is that there was another difference between Kaiser and myself, and it became more and more marked as I got to know him better. He was a hero; I became his disciple. I soon saw that he was better than I in all the ways that really mattered. He was strong and active, a very good athlete. He knew how to climb trees to perfection. I saw him go up a coconut palm once like lightning, without a loop of rope, like the copra[6] workers used, to help him; on my part I slid back down the trunk almost as soon as I started and had badly grazed hands for my pains. He could milk a cow. He did things which I would never dare to do. He shot humming-birds off the telephone wires when they settled there, an accurate master with his limewood catapult. I was horrified at this not only because I didn't like to kill birds but also because it was against the law to shoot humming-birds at all. They were talismanic in the island and rare and beautiful, and I was under the impression that you could go to prison for years if you killed one. I was timid. Kaiser laughed at the law. He shot them down and carefully collected their rainbow feathers, some like sunset in water, some a shimmering metallic green, some pale gold, others deep-sea blue, into match-boxes, just like a jeweller. He had many match-boxes full of humming-bird feathers. He offered me one of them once, ironically, I thought.

'What you 'fraid for? You 'fraid they going put you in jail or what!' He was always scornful when I showed I was timid.

'No,' I said, untruthfully, 'but I don't like them much. I prefer butterflies.'

'Go to hell then!'

And he pushed the match-box out of its cover with his forefinger and emptied all the lovely feathers on the ground. It was amazing how many there were crammed into the one small box. Now they scattered on the pitch road where we were outside the house like so many brilliant leaves. The gentlest of winds blew them yards they were so light and delicate. A few floated by chance into the gutter beside the road and, landing in the sluggish water there, moved slowly away like petals dropped from the samaan tree above us. I couldn't understand why he had done this. It seemed a little thing to get so annoyed about.

'What are you so vexed about, Kaiser?'

'Go to hell, eh! You white people too scornful, boy.'

'I don't understand what you mean at all.'

'It always so. You never going understand we. You is all right, you know, boy, but you is white.'

'All right, I'll take the feathers. Really and truly I like them, you know.'

'I not giving you a nex' box, boy. If you want, go and pick up in the gutter.'

He wasn't often like that. I looked on it just as a bad temper, a natural hazard. I would have to go easier if I wanted to learn from him all the things he had to teach.

Kaiser knew everything about birds. He knew their different songs and where they were used to lay their eggs. He showed me how to preserve their delicate and many-coloured shells intact for collection: at both ends you pierced each egg with a pin, then you blew out the contents, so that the eggshell was left dry and felt light as air in the hand. This was an operation which required extreme delicacy and many times, before I learnt properly, I shattered the eggshell while blowing it clean. As a result I had to practise on doves' eggs, which were the commonest (those of a mountain dove were a different matter), before Kaiser allowed me to try blowing a treasure like the egg of a humming-bird or a bluebird. When I could do these I was very pleased, put on many airs with my other friends. But Kaiser said with a great and healthy sneer:

'You still making you' pin-hole too dam' big. What you think you doing at all, boring wid a gimlet or what?'

One kind of bird he warned me about was the cassique. These were beautiful birds, some all yellow, some with scarlet backs. It was a temptation to raid their nests. But Kaiser told me the danger. These birds always hung their nests close to a marabunta's hive and seemed to have some contract with those vicious bees to guard against intruders.

'Tek care, boy. Watch out what you do. Cassique nes' an' 'bunta nes' look jus' the same. Don' stick up you han' near one so or you going get bite like a dog. I self had swell eye fo' two week one time fo' doing that same thing.'

After that I admired the yellow and the scarlet cassiques from a distance. He showed me how to make gum traps for birds. He slashed a breadfruit tree with a cutlass so that the white milk oozed out down the mottled grey trunk. He collected the milk in a tin cup, and when it had hardened into stickiness placed it on a twig near to some rich and rotting fruit, an already bird-pecked mango, a bee-sucked shaddock.[7] Often even if a bird was not quite caught it could do no more than fly feebly along, its wings sticky with the laglie,[8] its feet catching in any bush it settled on. Then Kaiser would run it down as it fluttered from place to place and wring its neck at once. For a long time I could not bear to see this; to me it was a hideous and cruel thing to do. As usual Kaiser would mock me for my faintheartedness.

'You is a minor mouse, boy, one minor mouse,' he told me once when I said he was bloodthirsty.

He was brought up with a different feeling from mine about these things. He saw no sense in being sorry for animals, or even in being kind to them unless it was a matter of necessity, like keeping a cow in good condition. He couldn't understand why we pampered and petted our dogs and cats. He was not sadistic in this matter – I never knew him to be cruel for the sake of being cruel, but his attitude was not more than one of indifference. He loved a few human beings, himself especially, and he could not see the point of bothering himself with diluted pastime loving. He was hardened through years of example in this attitude. Animals were beneath him; they were meant for his use and further than that not only he but generations before him in similar villages could not see. Many of the village families had a donkey, all had a cow, some had a dog for hunting; none had the green and talking parakeets of many of our drawing-rooms. So the birds that he caught in the laglie traps were more often than not for Kaiser good food which the same night his family could cook and eat. He told me that his father liked doves in particular. They were tender and their bones so small that he could chew and eat those too. In the end I came to see his point of view, but I could never at any time bring myself to wring a bird's neck, and I killed them only for their pretty feathers.

Kaiser was a deserving hero. He taught me an infinity of the tricks of a boy's trade. He showed me how to make a catapult – the best wood was lime or grapefruit – how to make bamboo flutes, whistles from the stalks of paw-paw trees. I was instructed by him in useful lore, like where to find the best fish-holes in the river, how to peel cane with the teeth. I admired him for his fund of forceful common-sense instruction. If I was attacked by a nest of Jack Spaniards,[9] he told me:

'Screw up you' eye, boy, and get to hell!'

Kaiser's magic exerted a strong hold on me. Sometimes he seemed to be in touch with a power which frightened me. There was one thing in particular I was frightened of. In his locker-room at the back of the house he kept a mountain dove's egg, blue as pale eyes, which he had blown himself. Through one of the pin holes he had put a grain of rice about as big as the hole. Once or twice he took me into the room and shook the blue shell for a minute or so, and he told me that the time the rice grain fell back through the hole the end of our world was near us and angels would root up even the Treasury Building in Port of Spain[10] and strangle all the people in the world with their golden fingers. This ceremony of shaking the dove's egg terrified me. It terrified him too. I remember the fear and tension in the dark little locker-room. Sweat poured down our faces. Two small boys stood at the centre of the universe controlling God. And even though I felt that the grain of rice dictated what He must do, I prayed God desperately in those minutes to keep the white tiny grain safe in the egg. Both of us sweated the minutes out as if they were the last before an execution. Then Kaiser would put the egg away and smile and sigh.

'God, Kaiser, why do you shake it at all? Don't shake it and it'll be all right. One day you might kill everybody.'

'Boy, you *mus'* shake it sometime. They *expec'* it. What you think would happen if we show we 'fraid of them, eh? No, boy, we mus'n't 'fraid them like that ... I going shake the egg sometime an' put a trus'...'

'Where? Where? Where're you going to put a trust? If the rice comes out it isn't God's fault, it's yours.'

'What you saying? It not my dam' fault. I not going be a dam' coward for nobody. You could get kill for that too besides. If you don' want to tes' brave what they want, don't come, eh.'

But I always went. It was a kind of joy to be suspended in fear. I felt a more important person. Kaiser and I were daredevils, risking everything. It was better than pretending to fight and conquer a thousand men.

Kaiser made me absorb certain necessary superstitions. If I ever stepped on a frog I must keep two of my fingers crossed all day or evil would befall. On the other hand, even to see a coral snake and far more to kill one, was the best of luck and I could expect fortune to smile on me for a long week. I was told, and faithfully believed, that if I ever found a perfectly smooth and oval stone I had only to place it in a jar full of water, cut a thumb, put a drop of blood in, and add one more drop every week: in a year's time that stone would turn into a beautiful and priceless ruby. Once I found a stone which I thought sufficiently smooth and round to try my fortunate knowledge on. I kept it a little over a month, religiously contributing the five beads of blood. I kept it in a secret drawer but my mother discovered it all the same. To my fury and amazement, even though I told her what it was for, how it could make our fortune, she discarded jar, rusty water, oval stone, all, where I could not find them again, comforting me with a gentle smile and two paradise plums. I never found another stone so round. Nor did Kaiser ever find one at all though he kicked even more earnestly than I at every river path we walked.

On another occasion he told me, his dark eyes serious and intent, as they always were when he talked of magic:

'Look, boy, I telling you this because I know what I saying. When it new moon tek up you'self and walk seven time roun' the tamarin' tree by Mister Godfrey. Befo' you know whe' you is you going grow hair like mad on you' ches' and get strong as Julius Caesar. True, man!'

This wasn't a success. I didn't grow any hair on my chest and remained weak as putty in comparison with Kaiser himself, who claimed that he had walked around Mr Godfrey's tamarind tree more than forty times.

Despite these occasional failures I did not in the slightest lose faith in Kaiser. He was the fount of all worthwhile knowledge; he was an initiate in the special mysteries of the world; he had magic in his fingers. He cursed bravely. He was strong and confident. He was a leader. He was a good friend.

What is more he was the brother of Jaillin. And Jaillin I loved.

GLOSSARY
1 *tamarind*: a medium-sized and well-known tree with a dense crown of feathery leaves, pale yellow flowers and dark red flower buds. It has long grey pods with dark brown edible pulp.
2 *immortelle*: flowers of papery texture which keep their colour after being dried.
3 *samaan tree*: a huge, canopied tree covered from spring to autumn with tiny pink-tipped tufts. In winter it has long black pods.
4 *coolie*: insulting word for 'Indian'.
5 *badjohns*: naughty boys.
6 *copra*: dried kernels of coconuts.
7 *shaddock*: grapefruit.
8 *laglie*: gumlike substance.
9 *Jack Spaniards*: wild bees or wasps.
10 *Port of Spain*: capital of Trinidad.

SUGGESTIONS FOR WRITING AND DISCUSSION

1 What does the comment 'important things like that' tell you about the narrator (Alan)?

2 Describe some of the boys' activities.

3 Copy out sentences spoken by Kaiser and sentences spoken by Alan. List their differences in pronunciation (as far as you can tell), use of language and vocabulary. How would you sum up the main differences in the way they speak? What do you see as the advantages and disadvantages of each way of speaking? Why do you think they speak differently?

4 Contrast the characters of Alan and Kaiser, and their positions in life.

5 Describe how Alan feels about Kaiser and why.

6 *Comment on the author's skill in bringing out the differences between Alan and Kaiser. (Note, for example, their different reactions to incidents, different beliefs, different attitudes to 'rules', different ways of speaking.)*

7 *Write a story about one child hero-worshipping another.*

8 *Do you think different accents and dialects are a good thing? Are there different accents/dialects in your area? Can you collect examples of some? (You will perhaps, in some cases, need to use a tape recorder and transcribe a few sentences.) What interesting differences can you find, and what points in common?*

9 *'He saw no sense in being sorry for animals or even in being kind to them.' Discuss Kaiser's point of view. How does it relate to some modern farming practices such as battery-hen farming?*

10 *Write your own episode of another day in the lives of Alan, Kaiser and (if you like) Kaiser's sister, Jaillin.*

11 *Write about friends of yours who have played an important part in your life. (You could describe their personalities, appearance, your quarrels, places you visited together, how you helped each other, and so on.)*

FURTHER READING

The Humming-Bird Tree Ian McDonald (Heinemann Educational Books)

EDWARD LUCIE-SMITH

Edward Lucie-Smith was born in 1933 in Kingston, Jamaica, and lived there until he was thirteen years old. He went to school in Jamaica, then in Canterbury, England, and finally read history at Oxford University. At one time an education officer in the RAF, he has worked as a photographer, translator and freelance journalist. He now lives in England and has established a wide reputation as a poet and art critic. His first collection of poems was entitled *A Tropical Childhood*. He has also written an autobiography entitled *The Burnt Child*.

A Tropical Childhood

In the hot noons I heard the fusillade
   As soldiers on the range learnt how to kill,
Used my toy microscope, whose lens arrayed
   The twenty rainbows in a parrot's quill.

Or once, while I was swimming in the bay,
   The guns upon the other, seaward shore
Began a practice-shoot; the angry spray
   Fountained above the point at every roar.

Then I, in the calm water, dived to chase
   Pennies my father threw me, searched the sand
For the brown disc a yard beneath my face,
   And never tried to see beyond my hand.

That was the time when a dead grasshopper
   Devoured by ants before my captive eye
Made the sun dark, yet distant battles were
   Names in a dream, outside geography.

SUGGESTIONS FOR WRITING AND DISCUSSION

1 *What point is the poet making about childhood and how does he make it?*
2 *Comment on the verse form in which this poem is written.*
3 *Assemble as much information as you can (including pictures where possible) about children who have had 'a turbulent childhood' (for instance, children in the Second World War in this country, children in Northern Ireland, in the Lebanon, children in a refugee camp or food centre in the Sudan, Ethiopia, or the western Sahara). Write your own poem or prose passage about such a child and call it 'A Turbulent Childhood'.*
4 *'. . . yet distant battles were*
Names in a dream, outside geography.'
Do you think children ought to know and be told about 'distant battles' or is it better to keep them innocent and ignorant of such things until they are older?

FURTHER READING

A Tropical Childhood Edward Lucie-Smith (Oxford University Press)
The Burnt Child Edward Lucie-Smith (Gollancz)

EDWARD KAMAU BRATHWAITE

Edward Kamau Brathwaite was born in Barbados in 1930. He was educated there and at Cambridge University. He taught for some years in Ghana before returning to the West Indies. He is a lecturer at the University of the West Indies, and is one of the most important poets at present writing in English. Brathwaite frequently recites his own work at poetry festivals, workshops, and on a variety of occasions. He has been influential in creating an awareness of the importance in the Caribbean heritage of spoken and performed poetry, and of poetry drawing its strength from folk forms and rhythms, as well as from the English literary tradition. His most important work is the trilogy *The Arrivants* (made up of *Rights of Passage*, *Masks* and

Islands). This explores the experience of Afro-Caribbean people through history. The spiritual dispossession involved, the wholeness and strength of aspects of the African universe, and finally the attempt to create a new synthesis and wholeness of vision are treated in turn in the trilogy.

DIVES

Before they built the deep water harbour
sinking an island to do it
we used to row out in our boats

to the white liners, great ocean-going floats,
to dive for coins. Women with bracelets,
men with expensive tickers on their wrists,

watched us through bland sun glasses
so that their blue stares never blinked.
they tossed us pennies. the spinning flat
metallic bird would hit the water with a little

flap and wing zig-zagging down the water's track.
our underwater eyes would watch it like a cat
as it dark bottomed soundwards like a pendulum
winging from side to side, now black

now bright, now black, now bright,
catching the dying daylight down
the coal dark tides of the ship.
every shadow we saw was a possible shark

but we followed that flat dark light
even if the propellers would suddenly turn
burning the water to murderous cold
we would never come nearer to gold

SUGGESTIONS FOR WRITING AND DISCUSSION

1 *Contrast the boy diving for coins in this poem with the boy described in 'A Tropical Childhood'.*
2 *Describe the way this poem is set out and comment on the way Brathwaite uses words (for example, his use of alliteration in such phrases as 'dying daylight down', and assonance, 'shadow ... shark', the contrast between light and dark, the force of the final rhyming couplet, and so on).*
3 *Write an account of some childhood activity that you enjoyed.*
4 *Write a conversation (in script form if you like) that might take place between the boy in the poem and his mother, after one of the 'dives for coins'.*
5 *Write an imagined conversation between two of the passengers as they watch the boys and perhaps throw coins for them.*

FURTHER READING

Rights of Passage Edward Kamau Brathwaite (Oxford University Press)
Masks Edward Kamau Brathwaite (Oxford University Press)
Islands Edward Kamau Brathwaite (Oxford University Press)

DANNIE ABSE

Dannie Abse was born in Cardiff in 1923. He trained as a doctor and has been a specialist in charge of the Chest Clinic of the Central London Medical Establishment since 1954. He has combined medical work with writing novels and several books of poetry. Since 1978 he has been President of the Poetry Society, London. His published books of poems include *After Every Green Thing, Walking Under Water* and *Collected Poems 1948–76*.

This passage is from *Ash on a Young Man's Sleeve* which is an account of growing up in a Jewish family in Cardiff during the 1930s. It describes a time when the author is a young schoolboy and just beginning to feel that in some important way he is apart and different from his Welsh companions.

A Poet in the Family is a further volume of autobiography.

WHAT'S IT LIKE TO BE JEWISH?

It was a winter's evening; Sidney was blowing on his hands. 'No more school till Monday,' said Sidney. It was silly to come home from school tea-time with the lamp-posts lit to keep away the ghosts. It was that cold: in the middle of the road, steam rose from a drain. We stood there, looking downwards, watching the steam rising. 'It's the devil smoking his pipe,' I said.

> *Adam and Eve and Pinchme*
> *Went down to the river to bathe.*
> *Adam and Eve got drownded.*
> *Who do you think was saved?*

A policeman came round the corner and we ran and we ran and we ran.
'You don't believe in Christmas, do you?' Sidney said to me.
'What's it like to be Jewish?' asked Philip.
''S all right,' I said.
'What's the difference?' demanded Philip.
'They puts 'ats on when they pray, we takes them off,' Sidney said.
'It's more than that, their blood's different,' said Philip, 'makes their noses grow.'
'Megan's coming round our house this evening,' I interrupted, making a face. Sidney and I didn't like girls because they wore knickers and Megan was especially silly. Lots of things were silly. Girls were silly, Miss Morgan our schoolmistress was silly, washing behind the ears was silly, going to bed early was silly. Now Philip was silly, because he didn't know what it was like to be Jewish. It wasn't anything really, except on Saturdays. We walked down the street wishing for snow and letting our breath fly from our mouths like ectoplasm. Soon it would be Christmas holidays, and presents and parties. The shops were crowded with voices. We pressed our noses against the window-panes, breathed, and wrote our names with our fingers on the misted glass. 'Leo loves Megan,' I wrote. It was all cotton wool in the windows, and the smell of tangerine peel, and a man with a long white beard.
'There's daft, i'n'it?' said Philip. 'Look, Father Xmas!'
'Where do flies go in the winter-time?' asked Sidney suddenly, and we all laughed sharing a secret.
When I arrived home, my brother Leo[1] was squeezing a blackhead from his forehead; then he combed his hair.
'Megan Davies,' I shouted at him. 'Megan Davies.'
'Do your homework,' he said.
'Who loves Megan Davies?' I cried.
He hit me harder than he meant for I fell against the wall and a bruise came up like an egg on my head.
'Put some butter on it,' my brother said, 'and stop crying.'
'Bloody, bloody, bloody,' I screamed at him.

'Now, then, enough of that,' he thundered. But the front door bell rang and he thought it was Megan, so I was given a penny to shut up.

It was only Uncle Isidore ... I don't think I've told you about him. I'd like to tell you. Of course, he's dead now, but I remember him quite well. He's become a sort of symbol really. You know, my parents still live in Wales, but we children have grown up and left home – as much, that is, as anybody can ever leave home. Anyway, when old Dafydd Morgan comes round the house at Cardiff these days, he and my parents get to talk about the kids.

'And what about Wilfred, your eldest son?' Old Morgan asks.

'All right,' says my father, 'not just an ordinary doctor but a psychiatrist.'

'Fancy,' says Morgan, 'Wilfred not just an ordinary doctor! Now my son Ianto 'e 'ad the gift do you know, just like his mother before she caught pneumonia, before she was ... exterminated, God rest her soul.'

'And Leo, my second son,' interrupts my father.

'Ah yes, Leo, Leo, there's a boy for you,' smiled Morgan. 'A boy in a million. Very spiritual. And a credit to you; goes to chapel, I mean synagogue, regular, I understand.'

'A solicitor, Mr Morgan, very clever.'

'Yes, very clever. Fancy, a solicitor! A very spiritual solicitor, I should think. Pays, I always think, to go to chapel – I mean synagogue. The connections do you know? Apart, of course, as a remedy for the spirit. But what about your third son, the youngest?'

'Our third son, Dafydd Morgan,' says my mother, 'is no good. Won't do any work.'

'Just like Uncle Isidore,' exclaim my father and mother, in unison, lifting up their hands hopelessly.

'Fancy,' says Morgan. 'Now my son Ianto ...'

Uncle Isidore wasn't exactly an uncle. Nobody knew his exact relationship to the family; but my parents called him 'Uncle', and my cousins called him 'Uncle', and my uncles called him 'Uncle'. He used to visit our home regularly, once a week, to collect his half a crown and eat a bit of supper. He went around all my relations' houses to receive a silver coin and grumble. It wasn't even as if he were a religious man. He just lived that way and the rest of the time he would read at Cardiff Central Library, or return to his dingy bed-sitting-room and play his violin. Not that he was a competent musician. On the contrary, he would scrape the easy bits and whistle the difficult phrases. That was his philosophy and his life. He always looked as if he needed a good wash, a shave, and a haircut. Uncle Isidore would pick me up and rub his face against my cheek. 'Like a baby's bottom,' he used to say to me. He smelt of dirt and tobacco. Eventually he died of kidney trouble. That's all I know about him. It doesn't seem very much. Uncle Isidore was just an oldish, untidy man, a sort of amateur beggar, who wouldn't work but read in the Reference Library and forever played his violin. It used to disturb people that he didn't have a reason for living. Dafydd Morgan would lecture him beginning with the inevitable sentence, 'The purpose of life is ...' and end up

his discourse hopelessly, saying, 'The Jews, bach,[2] are generally an indust-
rious people.' Now if Uncle Isidore had played his violin, say, like Yehudi
Menuhin, my parents would no longer say, 'Our third son is like Uncle
Isidore, what are we to do?' – but, rather, they'd exclaim, 'If only, oh, if only
our third son was like Uncle Isidore.' For I know that Uncle Isidore was an
artist, a real artist – except that he just didn't have the necessary accident of
talent. Yehudi Menuhin plays the violin and millions listen. Menuhin, thus,
has a purpose in life. But when Uncle Isidore played, even the cat would rush
for the door. Nobody listened. So, we say, he had no purpose in life. He was
contemptible, a rogue, an outlaw. I never cried when Uncle Isidore died.
Nobody did. There was a small funeral and my father and my uncles gave
some conscience money for his burial. That's all.

When the front door bell rang, Leo gave me a penny to shut up. He thought
that it was Megan Davies, but it was only Uncle Isidore.

'Workers of the world unite,'[3] grinned my uncle at my brother.

'You should talk,' Leo said.

'Leo hit me,' I said.

'What?' cried Uncle. 'That is coercion. We can't allow coercion.'

'But he gave me a penny,' I said.

'Then you're a rich lad,' he exclaimed, and looked so dismal that I offered
him the coin.

'That's all right, lad,' he said to me. 'I'll live without it.'

'Go on,' I insisted. 'Mama says you need it. Take it.'

'Ah,' said Uncle, 'your Mama is so right. She's a gentlewoman she is, and
do you know, lad, she used to be the prettiest girl in South Wales – Jewess or
Goy.'[4]

'She still is,' I said, big-eyed.

'No, no,' said Uncle. 'Now she's the most beautiful.' Yes, Uncle Isidore had
the soul of a gentleman.

The front door bell rang again.

'Megan Davies, Megan Davies,' I screamed.

Leo rushed to the door and I heard their voices together, and then the door
slammed. I was left in the house alone with Uncle Isidore. He kicked the fire
and the flames spat out of the coal, curling round his black boot. Mother
would return soon and cook the dinner. Philip was silly asking me what it was
like to be Jewish. Uncle Isidore stared into the fire with tremendous sadness.
I wasn't sure whether he was awake or asleep. It was silent in the room but for
the loud ticking of the mantelpiece clock. Suddenly he turned his head
towards the window.

'You could stand there,' he said vehemently, 'all your life and look out.' And
then he stared into the fire again. I walked over to the window, almost on
tiptoe, afraid to disturb him. I gazed out. Down the road I could see snow
falling under the lamp-post, and above, between the clouds, a few stars in the
cold sky.

'Uncle?' I asked.

'Well?'

'Uncle, what's it like to be Jewish all your life?' I asked.

''S all right,' he said, and for a moment we smiled at each other.

GLOSSARY

1 *Leo*: Dannie's brother, Leo Abse, became a Labour MP.
2 *bach*: dear (Welsh).
3 *'Workers of the world unite'*: a quotation from Karl Marx. Uncle Isidore is making fun of Leo's left-wing political views.
4 *Goy*: Gentile, that is, non-Jewish.

SUGGESTIONS FOR WRITING AND DISCUSSION

1 *Comment on the views Philip and Sidney have about Jews.*
2 *Give examples of how the author conveys the way young children think.*
3 *Describe Uncle Isidore.*
4 *Why does the narrator ask Uncle Isidore 'what's it like to be Jewish all your life'?*
5 *Comment on the style in which this extract is written (for example, the chatty, intimate, casual tone of the narrator, the use of dialogue, the humour).*
6 *Write about some of the games you used to play when you were younger.*
7 *Write a sketch of someone you know – or know of – whom other people regard as an 'outcast' or who is in some way 'odd' and different from others in your street or neighbourhood.*
8 *Uncle Isidore is seen as a hopeless case because he won't work; he has no fixed means of earning a living. What are your views on work? (For instance: Are some kinds of work worth doing but not others? Is work a* moral *necessity? A psychological* necessity? *Is work only a fashion, an ego-builder? Is work-sharing, when two people share the time and money for one job, a good idea? What about women who stay at home and don't 'work'?)*

FURTHER READING

Ash on a Young Man's Sleeve Dannie Abse (Penguin)
A Poet in the Family Dannie Abse (Hutchinson)
Collected Poems Dannie Abse (Hutchinson)

HAN SUYIN

Han Suyin is the pen-name of Elizabeth Comber. She was born in Peking in 1917. Her mother was Belgian and her father Chinese. She was educated at Yenching University, Peking, also at the University of Brussels and later London University. After qualifying in medicine she returned to Asia and worked as a doctor. In 1952 she published the widely acclaimed love-story *A Many-Splendoured Thing*, set in Hong Kong. Her book *The Mountains of Nepal* was written after she had attended the coronation of the King of Nepal in 1956.

The Crippled Tree is a mixture of autobiography, history and extracts from family diaries and papers. It describes what happened in China during the Revolution of 1911 and the

years of civil strife that followed in which different warlords struggled with each other for power. The story is continued in *A Mortal Flower* and *Birdless Summer*.

ROSALIE

'Rosalie,[1] Rosalie.'

Rosalie, who did not want to be named Rosalie, crawled still further away from the house with its calling voice, crawled into the spiky grass that was not as all-protective as it had looked. Her back bore the sun's heat, the strings of her straw hat cut into her neck, and there were flies, persistent, more prickly than the grass, lurching at her legs. 'The princess,' she continued, 'started swimming away from the castle. She swam swiftly, the clean cool water soothing her wounds ...' She made swimming strokes with her arms and legs, flat on her stomach. It was very uncomfortable. She removed two pebbles from under her, and continued swimming.

'Eldest Miss, your mother is calling, Eldest Miss.'

That was another voice, the voice of Liu Mah the nurse, who was fat and had the smallest, the most pointed bound feet that Rosalie had noticed. In fact, because Rosalie had been fascinated by Liu Mah's feet, she had jumped on one of them only a few days ago. Liu Mah had sat sewing on the veranda, one of her legs with its dainty foot encased in a neat black cloth shoe resting upon the other thigh, one foot on the ground, in the way peasant women sit when they are sewing. Rosalie, looking at the foot on the ground, had jumped on it with both her feet. Liu Mah had screamed in agony, holding her foot in her hand, big tears rolling down her fat cheeks, suddenly ashen with pain. Now Liu Mah waddled towards her on those two small stumps which supported her ample weight, her trousered legs stroked aside the grass, and Rosalie could see how each stone under the tiny soles made Liu Mah stumble. Liu Mah tried to raise the little girl.

Rosalie threw her arms round the legs in their black padded trousers. 'There loomed the saving rock, and the princess reached it, and threw her arms around it.' Oh no, corrected Rosalie to herself, rocks would be all spiky, hard. The princess couldn't do that, it would hurt. She ceased clutching Liu Mah, who was laughing, nearly falling, disengaging herself from the child's arms.

'Big Miss, didn't you hear your mother calling you? Go quickly, or Taitai[2] will be very angry with you.'

'She's always angry with me,' said Rosalie. 'And I don't like my name, Rosalie.'

'It is a very nice name,' said Liu Mah, 'Lo-sa-lee. Go quickly, Taitai is waiting with Second Miss. Second Miss is already dressed, and look at you.'

'My mother loves her, she doesn't love me.'

This was Rosalie's big dolorous secret, among those she held clutched, a secret half disbelieved at times, at others only too obvious. Now she gave it to Liu Mah, because she had hurt Liu Mah by jumping on her foot; but Liu Mah did not acknowledge the gift. People seldom knew when one gave them something. Even Liu Mah, whose gentle patient fatness was all the tenderness Rosalie was to remember, did not know she was being given something. She dusted Rosalie's dress.

'You must not say this, Big Miss! Of course, Taitai loves you. And your father, Laoyeh,[3] loves you best of all. But you are so wicked at times.'

'Papa is always busy.'

'Ah, but Laoyeh is a great gentleman. Without Laoyeh, there would be no rice in our bowls, no stick to our fire, no warmth under our beds.[4] Look at the railway, all of us depend on the iron road to eat rice.'

Rosalie went back with Liu Mah through the grass, up the slope, to the house. The house she was to remember as a large building on top of a hill. Below the hill was the railway station, the rails like a small maze, and the trains. All around, flat flat, the loess[5] plain of Honan, flat to the sky's limit. The house was red brick. It had been the house of a Belgian engineer, but now Papa had taken his place, the Belgian had gone, another one would come, and they would move to a small house. At the front door with its broad stone steps she turned to watch the glistening tracks dancing in the heat haze, and laying in wait upon the tracks, alive and understandable, the trains, grey smoke like breath couched upon them. At night she woke to listen to them, the pounding, the hoots, rending night with soft deliberation, like Liu Mah tearing unbleached cotton into long strips with which to bind tight her aching feet, every night.

'Ah, there you are at last,' said Mama, tying big white satin ribbons sent by Grandmama on to Tiza's pigtails, 'and dirty as usual. One would think you love dirt, dragging yourself in the mud.'

'Dirt is clean,' shouted Rosalie, enraged. 'Anyway, cleaner than you.'

Mama caught her a slap intended for the face, but it slipped on her hair instead. Rosalie, screaming, was led off by Liu Mah and put to bed, while Mama went off with Tiza, to call on Mrs Belloni, the wife of the Italian engineer, who lived in the next house.

For years Rosalie was to remember the desolate width of the bed that afternoon, with the two big lumpy pillows (one hers, one Tiza's) which she now drew over her face, hiding in the crevice between them, her nose a little out to breathe, but otherwise buried in plump whiteness, while she sobbed and knew the enormous, endless sorrow of childhood; while Liu Mah sighed as if she, Liu Mah, had also been punished, and rocked herself on the hard small stool by the bedside, and once in a while put out a patting hand to pat the pillows, not the child; and the gesture was more solace than any closer touch, for Liu Mah knew that the child detested being touched or hugged. Rosalie in bed thought she would scream, and exploded in such a paroxysm of screaming that she became frightened at the spasmodic clutching and

unclutching within her breast, and stopped. As her loud sobs became sys-
tematized and rhythmic and somehow appeasing, Liu Mah patted, and in the
interval she caught the smell of Liu Mah, the aroma of garlic and sweat which
she was to recover, time and time again, in China, in China, only in China; it
was the smell of love, selfless and detached, which made her go back and go
back to China, for nowhere was it like that smell; recapturing through this
smell the trance of childhood, more potent than any after-coming love, was
coming home, coming home to love and security.

'Oh, you naughty child, naughty Big Miss,' crooned Liu Mah, lullaby rather
than admonishment, 'you have made Taitai so angry. And now you scream
yourself ugly. And there is no one here but me to see you. What will Taitai
say?'

Rosalie, tranquil now, wept normally. 'Liu Mah, I am bad, bad, everybody
says I am bad,' and had another fit of sobs as she remembered Liu Mah's foot.

Together they saw the room darken with evening, and Liu Mah crooned
and washed Rosalie's swollen face and changed her clothes, meanwhile
keeping up the soft burr of her voice, so soothing. And then she brought
Rosalie downstairs, holding her hand, the child reluctant but keeping step,
for to be dragged behind Liu Mah would have been shameful; downstairs to
the living-room with its brown wooden floors, with the round table covered
with a white tablecloth, and the big lamp with its alluring blue glass body, and
round glass funnel with a soft cream shimmer, which flung into faces
shadows of not-themselves, transfiguring all.

Already Papa sat at the table, his boots in one corner, standing by themselves, like another Papa ready to tread the iron road, to make rice fill the bowl
of Liu Mah, and twigs for the fire under the beds. The boots were black, long
to the knee, there were straps below the knee-caps, and they had their own
smell and their own boot sound when they walked. Papa was ladling out the
soup, beef and turnips, and it smoked a little white cloud upwards from its
tureen, and inside the beef broth swayed oval big and small oil globules upon
its surface, like many eyes staring up. 'Eyes of sea serpents,' thought Rosalie,
starting on her self-told story again.

'Ah, there she is,' said Mama. 'Did I tell you' – she addressed Papa – 'what
the Wicked One said to me today?'

The Wicked One began more tears, they rolled down cheeks wooden with
crying. But inside herself she was not weeping, she was tired, and she waited,
her eyes upon her father. Would Papa too be against her?

Papa sighed, it was a sigh much sadder than Liu Mah's. 'You've told me.
Now, why are you so wicked?' His voice was monotonous with tiredness. It
was the warlords that made him so tired, they kept on stealing the engines
and the carriages from the railway.

'Sit down, sit down, Big Miss, now you must eat,' clucked Liu Mah, and
then her bulk was gone, leaving a sudden emptiness, and Rosalie was
swallowing her soup and licking her mouth sideways to catch a saltiness of
tears.

Tiza sat across the table, the loved one, still with her ribbons on, looking mildly at her big sister out of candid brown eyes. Mama cut bread and knifed butter on it, cut it in two and gave half to Tiza and half to Rosalie. Rosalie did not want to eat it. She was hungry, and had another plate of soup.

After supper Liu Mah undressed the children and put them to bed, and Mama came to the bed Rosalie and Tiza shared, the same one that Rosalie had rolled and screamed on in the hot afternoon. The nights were still cool, but the thick winter quilts had been changed to thinner ones, and there was a green and silver pattern on the top quilt. Liu Mah had sewn the quilts for the family in the previous autumn, laying a large white cotton sheet down upon newspapers on the floor, and on that placed the cotton wool wadding, padding it even by hand, tuft by tuft, flake by flake, until it was like a small snowfall upon the ground. Her ugly daughter, who had a very thick pigtail and only one eye, the other was an empty shut eyelid, having been put out by a blow from her father, helped her, picking out of the tufts small seeds or flecks of dirt left over by the carder. On the wadding they had then spread the silk top, six foot by four, tucked the cotton sheet round it, and sewn the two together with the hand-made thread of Honan, spooled by hand, thread which smelt so nice, twisted together, and waxed to make long-burning wicks. In the late spring Liu Mah would unpick all the quilts, wash the cloth lining and the silk separately; and the cotton wool padding, now matted, went to the village carder to be washed. The carder, with a great bow and metal string that went zing-zing-zing, sifted the newly washed matted lumps to make it all fluffy again, and then rolled it up and put paper round it and a twist of rope, and there it was, ready for next winter's quilt.

Tiza's hair was done up tight for the night in pigtails, because the next day was Sunday, when her hair, which reached below her shoulders, would spread out, waved stiffly for the morning service, which was only prayers, since there was no priest as yet, on this sector of the railway. Mama brushed and plaited the hair herself, and now the pigtails were in place upon the pillow, and she bent down, kissed Tiza, with her finger drawing a little cross upon her forehead, whispering: 'God bless you and keep you safe tonight.' Rosalie hardened herself as Mama came round the foot of the bed to her side, tucked the quilt in, and made a small cross on her forehead and said: 'God bless you and keep you safe tonight.'

Rosalie's hair was short and straight, ribbon always slid off it, even before the garden was reached. At night there was no brushing to make it shine, no plaiting for the next day. Once, long ago (so it seemed to her at four), she had said to Mama, who was brushing Tiza's hair: 'Brush mine, brush mine, Mama.' Mama had given it a few strokes, bringing the brush down hurriedly upon Rosalie's head, and there had been this feeling of hurry and distaste, and no pleasure; not the pleasure which made Tiza's eyes rounder and rounder, as with long slow strokes Mama brushed her hair. 'You never keep still, how can anyone brush your hair?' Mama said to Rosalie.

Tiza had many ribbons. 'When we get to Peking Papa will buy you a carved box for your ribbons,' said Mama to her.

The dark was around them, tucked like a quilt about them. In the dark a train hooted, melodious, comforting, half asleep. The big cupboard opposite the bed grew into its familiar night dragon shape, an embattled dragon keeping watch, and Rosalie picked up once more her story of the Princess. 'She drew herself out of the water, upon the beach, and out of the sea after her came Faithful Dragon. And before her eyes was a knight in armour, flashing gold, his sword one solid diamond.'

Thus Rosalie gave her unforgiving mind its rest, rocked to sleep, but not to forgetfulness, by the distant pounding of a train.

'A sister, a sister, it's a little sister!'

Shrieks from the bedroom were a little sister. Why Mama had to go to bed for a little sister was not clear. The doctor had come, a doctor from the French hospital; Mama hated all the French, since a French doctor had killed Sea Orchid, her son, but this doctor was a Greek; Mama said the Greeks were gentle, and good doctors.

The Greek doctor had an elongate black bag, a small beard curving over his chin which bobbed when he spattered talk, so that Mama called him the Goat, and his hair grew fiercely, very shining and curly. He had a big, pale, damp-haired daughter who had just been married to a French clerk in the French bank. Rosalie and Tiza had been to the wedding in St Michael's Church in the Legation Quarters. A few days later, Papa talking to Mama had said something about this girl being 'barred'. Rosalie was excited, especially when Papa had added, laughing, that she seemed 'to have a bone there'. A bone where? Why was she barred? From what? The bone, the beard, the doctor's bag and the French doctor who had killed Sea Orchid were jumbled in a trance of words, and it all ended into the fact that Sea Orchid had died because he was half-caste. Rosalie knew that she too was half-caste, and the big, pale, doctor's child was a half-caste too, but much less so than Rosalie, because her father was Greek and therefore European; her mother, who was Chinese, was kept hidden in the house, so that her daughter's chances in life might not be spoilt. In that way, it made her less half-caste. Everyone said the mother was so right to hide.

But this new little sister brought by the Greek doctor, what was she? Would she be Greek, or French since she came from the French hospital, or half-caste too? And in that case would she die? Not only Sea Orchid, but after Rosalie and Tiza were born, another little brother, another little sister, and yet another little brother; all had died, because they were half-caste, which meant the doctor might or might not bother to come. And a Chinese midwife delivered one brother, and dropped him on his head, so that he died two days later; a little sister had been infected with abscesses all over her body, and died screaming; and another brother became blue and died, and Mama had nearly died of bleeding too. That was when Papa was working, up and down the railways. Up and down, and right and left; first on the Lunghai railway, to push the line east from Hsuchow, west from Kaifeng. Rosalie knew all the names of all the stations along the Lunghai railway. This Papa had done for years, from 1913 to 1919. And then on the Peking–Hankow railway, down to Hankow on the Great River, up to Chengchow on the Yellow River, on to Hsinyang, and then to Changhsintien, and finally to Peking in 1921 or 1922.

Peking was a city, a big city at last, and Mama said: 'Now I can be looked after properly by a good doctor.'

Since the others had died because they were half-caste, how could a doctor prevent this new little sister dying? Doctors were wonderful people, like magicians in the stories, like the wizard Chuko Liang, like Wah Toh the clever physician who removed arrows without pain. Liu Mah was no longer there, but there was a Wang Mah now, thin and small and never smiling, her hands always dry, big feet because she was a Manchu,[6] and very cheap, eating very little. Wang Mah also told fine stories: of a boy walking to find the sun which had gone away in hiding, and fighting demons of the darkness on his way; another one about a girl who had a magic flute and people who heard its sound forgot their worries; and another about a woman who was really a beautiful white snake and who died for love. Wang Mah said that doctors were good spirits, the same as Buddha, and she herself believed much in taking medicines. Often she had headaches and appeared in the morning with little round pieces of paper stuck on her temples, and smelling of ginger.

The new little sister might live, with the doctor there, and in a big city. Rosalie and Tiza were taken into the bedroom, with its disinfectant smell. The candle flickered a hollow flame in its white enamelled candle-holder, which had a bit chipped off its round saucer bottom, showing the black iron underneath, the bit Rosalie thought nice to rub against her finger. Rosalie thrust her head against the mosquito net, which had a cottony smell and feel, and made a music when rubbed, as a comb did, a weak cicada noise. Everything had its own smell and feel and look and sound, and that was why it was good to be; and suddenly she was happy because there were so many things to feel and hear and smell and look at, like the mosquito net, or the smell and shape, colour and size, sound of this new thing, a little sister, a long red thing shrieking and black hair on its head, and the smell different from any other, and by its side Mama lying down, almost as if it was nothing to be brought a new baby. Why did she have to lie down because the doctor brought a baby in his bag? Rosalie eyed the bag, decided it was too small to put a baby in unless the baby was folded up inside. Folding things did make them smaller. She tried it with her doll next day, and it worked. Then for a while she had to play at having a baby, and folded herself into a large water jar in the courtyard, and was both baby and doctor, while Tiza became Mama and was made to lie down.

Tiza stared also at the little sister, her breath coming gently in and out. Tiza was so pretty now, and she wanted a kitten, and Mama had promised her one. She looked at the baby and said: 'Marianne.'

That was the name of her doll, with dark curly hair and a biscuit tint to her face. So the new sister was Marianne. Rosalie's doll had had her nose cut, her face washed, was so much the worse for it, and could not give her name to the new baby.

And now in the rickshaw, to go to the park in the morning, there was Mama

carrying Marianne, and Tiza and Rosalie standing by her knees on the footrest, a heavy load for a man to pull. The carriage was a secondhand one, bought when they had arrived in Peking. Feng, the rickshaw puller, was handsome, muscled shoulders most beautiful, skin like golden silk, hairless, and he pulled for six dollars a month. In the morning, for two coppers, he bought himself unleavened wheat bread, a big flat round slab of it, and ate it with a stick or two of raw garlic, and drank hot water. In winter he wore a padded gown that Mama had made for him. There were two copper lamps to the rickshaw, swinging on either side of the shafts, a bell underfoot with a push button of copper that Rosalie pressed her foot on and then it went ding-a-ling ding-a-ling, clearing a way along the dusty small intestinal *hutungs*[7] of Peking. The rickshaw seat was padded, there were slip covers of white cotton with frills which Mama ordered Wang Mah to wash and change once a week, because of the fleas and lice, Mama said. Mama did not allow Feng to sit in his own rickshaw seat because of the lice, he was to sit on the footrest, but that was comfortable enough because there was a small carpet upon which the feet of the sitter rested. No rickshaw owner allowed the rickshaw man, the man between the shafts, to sit in his own rickshaw seat because he might dirty it. Only outside rickshaws, those who did not have private owners, who rented their rickshaws from companies and prowled the streets for passengers and haggled over a copper, those sat and slept in their rickshaws, because they had no home, there was nowhere else for them to sit or sleep. They huddled in their rags in the winter, and Mama said their rickshaws were full of vermin, and one would catch the plague, bitten by lice, if one sat in a common rickshaw.

Remembered best after Liu Mah in after years was Feng, the rickshaw puller, remembered to the last detail because Rosalie knew he was beautiful. She looked at his back, saw the skin slide upon the slim strong muscles, the colour of the skin, and it was something to look at all the time, because Feng pulled off his top jacket to run; he sweated, and then it was more beautiful, like the sun going into rainpools. And yet it was never spoken of, and there was no way to say this beauty. Feng pulled smooth and fast, outdistancing other rickshaws, mocking them with his swift feet from which the dust flew, the rickshaw wheels with their shining spokes leaving two skipping fountains of dust behind them. Feng was even better than Balthazar,[8] even better than a train, for he went singing, 'Going north,' when he turned a corner, or 'Make light, make light,' when he passed another puller.

And because of Feng, there were all the rickshaws of Peking, all the possible Fengs. Through Feng all the other pulling men were seen, felt, heard, smelt, because they were, they existed, they did not disappear, like stories one could not remember the next morning because of a piece missing and no one to tell what was wrong. They made a world of fleet misery, beauty and squalor, a world running by on swift feet, or stumbling in rags, a brightness of bells and brass or a dingy broken-down panting; always a horror and a fascination, their backs, their backs naked and quivering, bones counted, flesh sweating its life out running. Never could one see their faces, and as they ran between their shafts one could shout, 'Faster, faster!' or stamp up and down to make them run. Their backs were terribly alive, and sometimes Rosalie thought: What would I do if I pulled a rickshaw? And she did, putting herself between the shafts, trying to lift and to pull, and Feng laughed softly, and stopped her, taking the rickshaw back to its shed. He slept on a plank behind the shed. He was lucky, Feng, being young and strong, and hired by a family for six dollars a month.

And alongside the gazelle (for so Mama called Feng) shuffled and limped and dragged all future Fengs, wizened, bent, smelly old men pulling carriages as ruinous as they, pulling as they had pulled since they were young like Feng, pulling towards a cold, verminous and wheezy death between the shafts.

One day Rosalie refused to sit in the rickshaw. It was because she had seen the death of a rickshaw man, so ragged that in death he seemed to come to pieces. A common death between the shafts, while Feng ran by. This rickshaw man was ahead of Feng on the way back from the East Market, and suddenly he toppled down, falling into his own heap of rags, and on him fell his passenger, a man in a long gown with a scarf round his neck and a felt hat square upon his head; and Feng coming behind nearly ran into them, only braked himself in time, skidding on cloth shoes, shouting 'Wai!'[9] to warn himself and others, and the shafts of his carriage he lifted up so quickly that Mama and the children fell backwards in their seat. Feng was so well built, skilful and careful, that the carriage did not topple entirely backwards, and they were only a little shaken, but Mama screamed and screamed, and immediately many people collected, and the man who had fallen on top of his dead puller also was shouting, and a crowd gathered to look, and then they turned the puller over, and someone said: 'Dead, he is dead.'

'Go home, quick, quick,' shouted Mama.

So Feng picked up the shafts again and lifted and ran past the dead man, and a little along he laughed and said: 'He died, Taitai.'

'Don't talk. Run, quick, home,' shouted Mama.

And Rosalie pressed on the bell button with her foot and shouted: 'Kwai, kwai,' – quick, quick. So they ran homewards.

The next day Rosalie did not sit in the rickshaw, and the night after Tiza woke screaming in a nightmare. But after a while it was over, and they went as usual in the rickshaw.

The Central Park was a favourite place for children to play in, and Mama went there nearly three times a week, sometimes four times, in the short spring, after the dust storms, and in the early morning of the hot summers, through the autumn until it became too cold. There stories became games, acted out as they were talked with Tiza, with other playmates.

To get to the park, after coming out of the maze of *hutungs*, grey, dusty, uneven between the loping grey walls of houses, one emerged on to the old imperial way, paved with enormous blocks of stone diagonally set. The main gateway of the red-walled Forbidden City was the Gate of Heavenly Peace, facing the midday sun; and from there a paved road led straight to the Temple of Heaven. In the great square before the Gate of Heavenly Peace there were soldiers, soldiers with cutlasses on their backs; and not only there, but everywhere about Peking were soldiers, and in the Legation Quarters were foreign soldiers, each in front of their own legation gates. Everyone made a wide detour, well before reaching any soldier of any kind, for it was not good to get too near a uniform, any uniform. There were very few cars, and if one came, klaxoning, lunging on the road, everyone got out of the way quickly, for it was sure to be a warlord or a warlord's underling, and if one were run over nothing could be done about it. Standing on the footboard on both sides of the warlord cars were hired bodyguards, revolver at the hip, and sometimes, if they thought someone in the crowd was looking at them, they shot at him, or at the passers-by if they got excited, and no one could say anything, one merely ran for cover. These bodyguards were not Chinese, but so often White Russian, for it was a fashion of the warlords to hire White Russian bodyguards, and they were even worse, being more excitable than others.

When Papa returned home in the evening from his office with news of yet another warlord entering in triumph into the city of Peking, and when Peking prepared to receive the warlord with archways of paper flowers, and the citizens were stopped on the streets by soldiers for money for welcome gates and soldiers' comforts, when klaxoning cars ran the streets shooting and shouting, then Mama would tie a little flag, the red yellow black flag of Belgium, her own country, upon the rickshaw carriage when she took her children to the park.

And one day as they alighted in front of Central Park a European man leading a child by the hand stopped to stare at them getting out of the rickshaw, and said, very loud, looking at the flag, then at Mama carrying Marianne, at Rosalie and Tiza: 'Look, Peter, these are half-castes.'

Rosalie stared at him, and he was European, and the child was European too. Mama said: 'Come, my children, come,' and they entered the park. Across the flat sandy space where acrobats and shadow boxers practised, to the pine-planted man-made rocky hillocks where they played so many wonderful stories, Rosalie heard the word, a noise not to be smelt or palpated, no sound or look about it, the word. She knew it already, but somehow it had become new, the way the man had said it. And it made Mama different: Mama clutched her hand tighter as they walked, and it was the tight clasp of something fierce and gentle, like love, and suddenly Mama said:

'You look European, my children, you look like me.'

And the sun kicked the grey slate tiles of the pavilions among the rocks, and a grey-blue Peking magpie flew away.

And that was all it meant: half-caste, and Sea Orchid dying, and all the others dying. It was Papa being Chinese, and to be a Chinese in China was wrong, only being European was right. So Rosalie took the rickshaw's Belgian flag in her hand, and led troops to fight the dirty Chinese that day, since she looked European, she looked like Mama, so Mama had said.

GLOSSARY
1 *Rosalie*: the author, Han Suyin.
2 *Taitai*: Mistress of the house.
3 *Laoyeh*: Master of the house.
4 *under our beds*: 'Because of the intense winter cold, beds in North China are
   platforms of cement with a stove arrangement below. One sleeps on an oven top.'
   (Author's note)
5 *loess*: deposit of fine light-coloured wind-blown dust.
6 *Manchu*: member of Tartar people of north-east China.
7 *hutungs*: the name given to the narrow streets of Peking.
8 *Balthazar*: Rosalie's rocking horse.
9 *Wai!*: Watch out!

SUGGESTIONS FOR WRITING AND DISCUSSION

1 *Describe how Mama behaved towards Rosalie on the one hand and Tiza
  on the other. Are there any hints in the passage to suggest why this was?*
2 *Describe the impression you get of Rosalie from the first section of this
  extract.*
3 *Pick out some of the childish misconceptions Rosalie had.*
4 *Pick out some of the details that show that Rosalie was aware of her
  senses and used them.*
5 *Sum up the views expressed here about 'half-castes'. What do you think
  about these views? What would you say were the advantages and disadvantages of having parents of different races?*
6 *What evidence is there of discrimination against Rosalie's family (for
  example, when Rosalie's brothers and sisters were born)? What advantages did the family enjoy as well?*
7 *Describe Liu Mah, Wang Mah and Feng, and the feelings Rosalie had for
  each of them.*
8 *Write an impression of life in China at that time from what you learn
  from this extract.*
9 *Write about your childhood memories.*
10 *What impression do you have from this extract of the status of women in
   Chinese society at that time? What is their status in contemporary
   China?*
11 *Write your own story of two brothers, or sisters, who are very different
   from each other. (If you like, one could be the family favourite, as in this
   extract.)*

FURTHER READING

The Crippled Tree Han Suyin (Panther)
A Mortal Flower Han Suyin (Panther)
Birdless Summer Han Suyin (Panther)
A Many-Splendoured Thing Han Suyin (Panther)

SEAMUS HEANEY

Seamus Heaney was born in
1939 and grew up in County
Derry in Northern Ireland. He
was educated at Queen's
University, Belfast, and has
been an English teacher and a
university lecturer. One of the
central strands of Heaney's
poetry is his attachment to
country life, another is his
concern for the poor, the
disfranchised and the
dispossessed. He is one of the
most gifted contemporary poets
writing in English. His books of
poetry include *Death of a
Naturalist*, *Wintering Out*,
Field Work and *Selected Poems*,
published in 1980.

DEATH OF A NATURALIST

All year the flax-dam festered in the heart
Of the townland; green and heavy headed
Flax had rotted there, weighted down by huge sods.
Daily it sweltered in the punishing sun.
Bubbles gargled delicately, bluebottles
Wove a strong gauze of sound around the smell.
There were dragon-flies, spotted butterflies,
But best of all was the warm thick slobber
Of frogspawn that grew like clotted water
In the shade of the banks. Here, every spring
I would fill jampotfuls of the jellied
Specks to range on window-sills at home,
On shelves at school, and wait and watch until
The fattening dots burst into nimble-
Swimming tadpoles. Miss Walls would tell us how
The daddy frog was called a bullfrog
And how he croaked and how the mammy frog
Laid hundreds of little eggs and this was
Frogspawn. You could tell the weather by frogs too
For they were yellow in the sun and brown
In rain.

Then one hot day when fields were rank
With cowdung in the grass the angry frogs
Invaded the flax-dam; I ducked through hedges
To a coarse croaking that I had not heard
Before. The air was thick with a bass chorus.
Right down the dam gross-bellied frogs were cocked
On sods; their loose necks pulsed like sails. Some hopped:
The slap and plop were obscene threats. Some sat
Poised like mud grenades, their blunt heads farting.
I sickened, turned, and ran. The great slime kings
Were gathered there for vengeance and I knew
That if I dipped my hand the spawn would clutch it.

SUGGESTIONS FOR WRITING AND DISCUSSION

1 *Describe the atmosphere the poet builds up in this poem. Pick out some of the words and details which help to create this atmosphere. (Note his use of adjectives such as 'clotted' and of unusual phrases such as 'gauze of sound'; note, too, the contrast between the first and second sections of the poem.)*

2 *Explain why the boy 'sickened, turned, and ran'.*
3 *Write a story about a child who is afraid.*
4 *'The great slime kings/Were gathered there for vengeance'. Write a science fiction story with the title 'The Day the Frogs Took Over'.*

THE BARN

Threshed corn lay piled like grit of ivory
Or solid as cement in two-lugged sacks.
The musty dark hoarded an armoury
Of farmyard implements, harness, plough-socks.

The floor was mouse-grey, smooth, chilly concrete.
There were no windows, just two narrow shafts
Of gilded motes, crossing, from air-holes slit
High in each gable. The one door meant no draughts

All summer when the zinc burned like an oven.
A scythe's edge, a clean spade, a pitch-fork's prongs:
Slowly bright objects formed when you went in.
Then you felt cobwebs clogging up your lungs

And scuttled fast into the sunlit yard.
And into nights when bats were on the wing
Over the rafters of sleep, where bright eyes stared
From piles of grain in corners, fierce, unblinking.

The dark gulfed like a roof-space. I was chaff
To be pecked up when birds shot through the air-slits.
I lay face-down to shun the fear above.
The two-lugged sacks moved in like great blind rats.

SUGGESTIONS FOR WRITING AND DISCUSSION

1 *How does the poet make the boy's fear vivid?*
2 *Write a description of a place or a building that is mysterious or frightening.*
3 *'. . . nights when bats were on the wing*
   Over the rafters of sleep . . .'
   Write a story about a dream you had after visiting an old or disused building. Give it the title 'Nightmare'.

MID-TERM BREAK

I sat all morning in the college sick bay
Counting bells knelling classes to a close.
At two o'clock our neighbours drove me home.

In the porch I met my father crying –
He had always taken funerals in his stride –
And Big Jim Evans saying it was a hard blow.

The baby cooed and laughed and rocked the pram
When I came in, and I was embarrassed
By old men standing up to shake my hand

And tell me they were 'sorry for my trouble';
Whispers informed strangers I was the eldest,
Away at school, as my mother held my hand

In hers and coughed out angry tearless sighs.
At ten o'clock the ambulance arrived
With the corpse, stanched and bandaged by the nurses.

Next morning I went up into the room. Snowdrops
And candles soothed the bedside; I saw him
For the first time in six weeks. Paler now,

Wearing a poppy bruise on his left temple,
He lay in the four foot box as in his cot.
No gaudy scars, the bumper knocked him clear.

A four foot box, a foot for every year.

SUGGESTIONS FOR WRITING AND DISCUSSION

1 *Explain what has happened.*
2 *Comment on the style in which this poem is written and the kind of
   language the poet uses (for instance, the apparent lack of emotion on the
   part of the narrator, the very precise details of things seen and heard).*
3 *Compare this poem with either* 'Death of a Naturalist' *or* 'The Barn'.
4 *Write about a funeral, or a wake, that you have attended.*

FURTHER READING

Selected Poems Seamus Heaney (Faber)

GUERNSEY

G. B. EDWARDS

Gerald Basil Edwards was born
in Guernsey, Channel Islands,
in 1899 and died in 1976. He
served in the Royal Guernsey
Light Infantry during the First
World War, and worked as a
lecturer and civil servant. In
later life, he became something
of a recluse and very little is
known about him. *The Book of
Ebenezer Le Page* is the only
book he wrote. It is the account
of an old Guernseyman who
lived on the island from before
the Boer War until the 1960s.
The book was not published
until 1981, having been rejected
by many publishers. It is written
in the colloquial speech of the
main character with many
French undertones.

GUERNSEY CHILDHOOD

I had a good education, me. I went to the Vale School for Boys until I was twelve. I can see the old schoolroom yet: the broken-down desks and the worn-out forms with knots in that got stuck into your backside and the picture of the old Queen on the wall and of Jesus Christ walking on the water and the jam-jar of tadpoles on the windowsill. The Headmaster was Mess[1] Henri Falla from La Moye. He taught us Scripture first lesson in the morning; and Reading, Writing and Arithmetic later in the day. The Scripture didn't count. All we had to do was to sit still and listen, and it went in one ear and out the other; but Reading, Writing and Arithmetic we had to learn. Mess Falla was a good schoolmaster: he taught with the stick in his hand. If I said '2 and 2 is 5', he would shout 'Come out, Le Page[2] E!' There was Le Page A, B, C, D, E, F, and G in the school. I was Le Page E. 'Bend over! Touch your toes!' he would say: '2 and 2 is 4!' Whack! Whack! Whack! 'That'll learn you!' It did, you know. He didn't do it to hurt.

Miss Emily Tostevin did, though. She had a down on me. I don't know what for, I'm sure; because I never said a word. I would just sit with my arms folded and look at her. She said I was cheeky. 'Come out in front for impudence, Ebenezer Le Page,' she'd say. I would go out in front: bend over, touch my toes. She thought that was rude. 'Stand up!' she'd say. 'Hold out your hand: your LEFT hand!' She would only hit boys on their left hand, or, after, they made out they couldn't write. She didn't use a cane, but the edge of a ruler; and, golly, she knew how to hurt with it, too! I learnt the trick of holding my hand out sideways and lowering it the same time as the ruler came down: then I would rub it hard under my arm-pit and wrinkle up my face as if I was going to cry, so as she wouldn't know it hadn't hurt much.

She taught us History, Geography and Nature Study. History was dates. I have forgotten most of it now, but I know it began in 55 BC when Julius Caesar landed in Britain; and I remember AD 1066, because that was the year we conquered England.[3] Geography was the countries and capitals of Europe and the capes and bays of England. Some of the countries of Europe have changed since then, I think; but, as far as I know, the capes and bays of England are the same. Nature Study was the only thing I did right for Miss Tostevin. She gave me ten out of ten once for my composition on 'The Life of the Frog'.

I had to go to Sunday School as well. That was a nuisance. I would much rather have been flying my kite on the Common, or gone down on the beach; but I wasn't allowed to fly my kite on a Sunday, and if you went down on the beach, people said you was a heathen. There was one good thing about Sunday School; and that was there was nothing you had to learn. They made you sing hymns: 'Onward, Christian soldiers!' or 'Fight the good fight with all thy might!' or 'Trust-and-obey-there-is-no-other-way-to-be-happy-in-Jesus-but-to-trust-and-obey', while they took up a collection for Foreign Missions.

My father used to give me a penny for that; and I always put it in the box. I was honest. The Headmaster, he was called the Superintendent, prayed and read a chapter from the Bible; and then there was Announcements, but I never listened to those. After that came the Lesson. The boys was sorted out, a dozen or more in a class according to their ages; and each class sat on forms making three sides of a square. The Sunday School teacher sat on a chair in the open side and told the class a story with a moral.

I got into bad trouble at Sunday School. There was boys and girls in the same room in that school, the boys on one side and the girls on the other; and down the middle of the room the boys' classes and the girls' classes was back to back. A Mr Johns from on the Bridge was our teacher, I remember; and he had a long straggly moustache, and when he spoke he spat. I had to sit right back so as not to have a shower of his spit all over me. It happened on that Sunday I was sitting back to back with Marie Le Noury. I thought she was lovely. She was wearing a tight blue velvet frock and was well developed for a girl and had rosy cheeks and sly black eyes; and when I looked round, she looked round and smiled at me with those sly black eyes. I thought I would write her a little note. I had a stub of pencil in my pocket and tore a page out the back of my hymn-book and wrote, 'Je t'aime,[4] Marie.' I dug her in the ribs and she took the note and the pencil. I thought she would write back 'Je t'aime, Ebenezer', but instead I heard her saying, 'Look, Miss Collas, what one of the boys has given to me!'

Her teacher was a Miss Collas from The Hermitage. She was an old maid and I am not surprised. She looked as if she had been brought up on the vinegar bottle. Mr Johns stopped telling his story with a moral and all the other classes stopped listening to their teachers. 'Who gave you this?' said Miss Collas. 'Him!' said Marie and turned round and pointed to me. My heart broke. Miss Collas was holding my poor little love-letter with the tips of her fingers, as if it was too dirty to touch. 'Disgusting!' she said and got up and put it under the nose of the Superintendent, old Peter Le Maître. 'One of your boys is interfering with my girls,' she said. Old Peter Le Maître was a big man with a big face and big spectacles, and sat at a high desk at the top end of the room. 'Who wrote this?' he said. 'Ebenezer Le Page!' screamed all the girls. 'Come here, Ebenezer Le Page!' said old Peter. I went and stood in front of his high desk. He looked at me over the top of his spectacles; and he looked at my note through his spectacles; and looked at me again over the top of his spectacles. 'Is this what you come to Sunday School for?' he said. 'I don't know, sir,' I said. 'Go and stand in the porch!' he said. I went out to the porch with my tail between my legs; and then I said to myself, me: 'Bugger you, old Peter Le Maître!' and put on my cap and walked out.

I never looked at Marie Le Noury again. She married Reg Symes, an English chap in the Artillery stationed at Castle Cornet. He was a great boy with the Indian clubs[5] and used to give displays at military concerts; but he came out of the Army to please her and opened a little shop in the Commercial Arcade for mending clocks and watches. He worshipped the ground she walked on. When she got to middle age she left him and went to live with her married daughter in England; and he put his head in the gas oven and was found dead in the morning. I was lucky, really.

I went home round Birdo, so as not to be back too soon. There was an old man sitting on a rock with a spy-glass. I wondered what it was he was looking at; and then I noticed a young chap and a girl had managed to get themselves cut off by the tide on the Hommet and was curled up together on the grass. I couldn't see what they was doing; but the old man could see, him. I thought it was a funny way for an old man to pass his Sunday afternoon. I went round by the Vale Mill; but the big vanes wasn't turning. The cows was chewing the cud in the field. When I got indoors, my father asked me what the golden text was for that Sunday. He always asked me what the golden text was to make sure I hadn't played truant. I told him. 'Love thy neighbour as thyself.' He said, 'Well, if you do that, son, you can't go far wrong.' I had my doubts about that.

I didn't go to Sunday School again. I left the house the same time as if I was going and took the penny my father gave me for the Foreign Missions. I was sorry to have to steal that penny from my father; but what else could I do? I went and sat on the gate of L'Ancresse Common by the Vale Church with the boys from round there. In those days there was hundreds of sheep loose on the Common and the gate had to be kept shut, or they would have strayed all over the Parish. It was a nuisance for the gentry who wanted to drive across the Common in their carriages. They had to get down and open the gate and get back up and drive through and get down again and close the gate behind them. The boys was good. They would open the gate when they saw a carriage coming and close the gate behind it: then run after the carriage, calling out 'Apenny, please! Apenny, please!'

Sunday afternoons was a good time for making money on the gate; because the Townies, who was all gentry on Sundays, liked to drive out to L'Ancresse Common in their carriages to look at the sheep. I will say some of them was honest and would throw a halfpenny, and there'd be a run and a fight for it; but there are always some mean people in the world. The gentleman would pull a handful of change out of his pocket and say, 'Sorry, haven't got a halfpenny. Have you, my dear?' The lady would rummage in her handbag and say, 'I am afraid I haven't, darling.' By that time we'd have run after the carriage nearly to the Druid's Altar. Goodness, a penny would have done!

I had to keep my eyes skinned for some boy who had been to Sunday School, so as I would know what the golden text was for that Sunday. I usually managed to nab Bill Rihoy, who lived at L'Islet; but I don't think he always remembered it right. Once he told me it was 'An eye for an eye and a tooth for a tooth.' When I repeated it to my father, he said, 'Well, if that's what they teach you in Sunday School, soon there won't be many of us with any eyes, or any teeth, left.' As I have said before, he got some funny ideas in his head, my father.

I put the money I made in my money-box. I didn't tell a soul: not even my sister. It wasn't she was a tell-tale. She was the most honest and straight-forward girl and woman I have known in my whole life. She was so honest and straightforward you had to be careful what you said to her. The first thing I remember in this world is putting a penny in my money-box. I can't have been more than three or four. I earnt it for picking slugs off the cabbages. My father would give me a penny for twelve slugs and drown them. It was good money, when you come to think of it. My father was good that way. He believed in paying for everything and paying on the dot. From the time I was ten I earnt extra money cracking stones. My father knew Bert Le Feuvre, the foreman of Griffith's yard, and there was a little heap of spawls[6] waiting ready every night in summer after school for me to crack. I was paid a shilling a week for that and my father let me keep it.

I knew to a penny how much I got in my money-box. When I had ten pennies I'd shake them out and change them for a franc. I kept a lookout for English pennies because I could get thirteen Guernsey pennies for twelve of those. I was only a boy at school yet when I had over a pound in my money-box. On the Ash Wednesday, when we had holiday from school, I trotted into Town on my own and walked into the Old Bank and plonked down on the counter twenty-one Guernsey shillings in pennies and halfpennies and fippennies and francs. The chap behind the counter looked over at me and counted my money and pushed me across a sovereign. I had a golden sovereign in my money-box. I was rich!

I suppose I would have gone to work in the quarries and perhaps done well, if something awful hadn't happened at the Queen's quarry. Young Emile Thoumine was killed in the pit. He was only nineteen and hadn't been married three months. It was said the blasting must have loosened the side of the quarry, or water trickling down. Anyhow, a great block of granite came toppling over without warning and crushed him. I had never seen my father so upset as when he came in that evening. He was early because old Tom Mauger was with the doctor bringing up in the horse-box what was left of poor Emile; and he had asked my father to go in the trap and break the news to the young wife. They lived in Town. When my father told my mother what had happened, she said, 'What did he belong to?' She meant was he Church, or Chapel, or what; so as she would know where he was going to. I saw my father clench his fists; and I think, if she had been a man, he would have knocked her down. 'The man is dead!' he said. 'Come with me, son!'

I was pleased and excited to be going with my father in the trap. It was beginning to get dark and, while he was harnessing the pony, I lit the big candles in the lamps. It was rough along the front and the sea was coming across the road by the gas-works and over the Salerie Corner. The house was in the Canichers. It was too narrow for the trap to go up and my father tied Jack to the lamp-post at the corner and told me to stop there and mind him. I felt very sad left there all by myself and talked to Jack. I remember the flickering gas-light and the round shadows on the road and a big old tree dropping leaves and the wind blowing them about. My father wasn't long

gone. When he came back all he said was, 'She is with her mother.'

When we got home and was having our supper, my father said to my mother, 'Our boy is not going to work in the quarries.' 'What, then?' said my mother. 'We must find something better for him to do than that,' he said. I don't know if it was better, I don't think it was; but when I left school he got me a job in Dorey's Vineries. They was still growing grapes, but trying out tomatoes under the vines. I thought tomatoes was a funny sort of fruit. I didn't like the taste much. I liked the grapes, though. It turned out there was a better sale in England for the tomatoes and in the end the greenhouses grew nothing else.

I had to do what my father said; but, when he'd gone, I used to chuck it sometimes and go fishing for a spell. I was happier working out-of-doors and in a boat; but you can't trust the sea, and the fishes get ideas into their heads and sometimes they are where they ought to be and sometimes they are not. The tomatoes are always there, so back I would go; but, golly, it was hot in those greenhouses! Ah well, I was born to trouble as the sparks fly upwards. I earned my bread by the sweat of my brow.

GLOSSARY
1 *Mess*: Monsieur.
2 *Le Page*: a very common name in Guernsey.
3 *we conquered England*: the Guernsey Islanders are of French descent.
4 *Je t'aime*: I love you.
5 *Indian clubs*: bottle-shaped clubs used in gymnastics.
6 *spawls*: stone chips or splinters.

SUGGESTIONS FOR WRITING AND DISCUSSION

1 *Describe the kind of education Ebenezer had. What are your views on it?*
2 *Write a description of the kind of person Ebenezer was.*
3 *Ebenezer often comments wryly on his experiences. Pick out three such comments and explain how they reflect his point of view and reveal his character.*
4 *Comment on the style in which this extract is written (for instance, the way the writer gives the impression of someone talking and reminiscing).*
5 *How does the author manage to convey the impression of an old man remembering his childhood?*
6 *Choose one of the incidents described here and expand it into a story.*
7 *What do you think of the maxims 'An eye for an eye, and a tooth for a tooth', and 'Love thy neighbour as thyself'? Are they practical? Are they equally sensible?*
8 *'I earned my bread by the sweat of my brow.' Choose one type of work where this is true. Describe in detail what the work involves; what the pay or range of pay is; how you train; the strong and weak points of such work.*
9 *Try to interview an older person about his or her childhood and write it up, or give a presentation to the class and play back extracts from a recording of their memories. (If you interview someone who has lived in your area all their life you could ask what it was like when they were growing up.)*

FURTHER READING

The Book of Ebenezer Le Page G. B. Edwards (Hamish Hamilton)

EMLYN
WILLIAMS

Emlyn Williams was born in
Wales in 1905. He is an actor,
dramatist and theatre director.
Among his plays are *The Late
Christopher Bean, Night Must
Fall* and *The Corn Is Green*. He
has also written on the subjects
of law enforcement and prisons
and has written novels and short
stories as well as plays. In recent
years he has given one-man
performances of the works of
Charles Dickens and Dylan
Thomas.

George is an account of his early
life. This passage shows the
young George determined to
master spoken English. He then
wrestles with French and finds,
to his surprise, similarities
between his native Welsh and
the French language. The
situation described in the
extract chosen here was also
used in his play *The Corn Is
Green*. His autobiography is
continued in *Emlyn*.

MOVING UP

The spring term, there was harder weather to fight, but I was hardening too. Life in Form One settled down almost into dullness. Latin progressed too slowly for me: through the partition I heard Form Two reciting the third conjugation and longed to be there. English I enjoyed, but my pleasure was marred by my attitude, inside but more and more defined, towards Totty and the Flint[1] lot; a mixture of envy and contempt. Envy for their Philistine insouciance and prowess at games, particularly sunny Wally's; and contempt for their speech.

I did not talk much at school, except Welsh with Welsh boys, partly through shyness but mostly for another reason. Apart from my absorption in the written word, my instinct somehow was to speak English well and with as pure an accent as possible, neither drawled nor falsely refined; I was determined not to talk like Totty and Wally. The morning greeting of the Flint lot was ''ow-do', and 'ta-ra' was Flintese for 'good-bye', which would have sounded affected if not effeminate. In between ''ow-do' at nine and 'ta-ra' at four, there shuffled a conversational stream choked with banal flotsam which not all the Miss Cookes in Christendom could have sifted away. 'Oh 'eck,' Totty would say, 'you *are* flippin' 'alf-baked....' The girls talked better, but that could hardly help me. One day, walking out to football after Geography, Wally said, 'What the bloomin' 'eck is the name o' them thingummyjigs on a roof?' I said, 'Isn't the official name weather-vane?' 'Official,' scoffed Totty without malice, ''ark at the flippin' walkin' dictionary!' I blushed back into my shell.

On paper, though, I showed off. 'Invent three sentences to include inordinate, vehemence, parsimonious.' Wally's approach to this lacked the dash and accuracy of his footwork on the field: 'The teacher inordinates the class to write, if you talk a lot it is vehemence, people that study grammar and that are parsimonious.' I had just read an article in the *News of the World*, and for good measure worked all three words into one sentence. 'Rasputin, eerie werewolf of all the Russias, staggered up to the Czarina, his filthy locks inordinately matted as with the vehemence of the fanatic he flung a mere kopek to the subservient servant for he was a parsimonious monster.' But I confined my gymnastics to the ruled line, and it made me proud of the Ffynnongroew lot, Welsh to the core, that they showed none of my inhibitions. While I splashed knee-deep in the shallows of English, Septimus Luke Evans, without a flicker of his Savonarola[2] mask, the clown-priest, dived headlong into the torrent. 'It iss of our surmissation,' he would boom, holding his lapels and making a square meal of every word in front of Totty and Wally and the world, 'that the effluvia from that part of this edifrice nominated "Shanghai" cannot be assignated to pupils but to Staff and therefore not of human origin, next case pleess....' He had them foxed; grasping English like a nettle, he uprooted it.

Subject for Composition: 'The East'. I remembered *The Great White Slave* and felt at home. 'Tibet is the roof of the world, and is very enigmatic. It is the cradle of Buddhism. It is more interesting than our religion, and a study of it would not impair us, it would be good to be impartial. Buddha was an exceedingly first-rate man. . . .' Then followed – from an impartial unimpaired authority, 1000 hours in chapel – a detailed account of Buddhism. ''Ow d'ye spell crocodile?' whispered Wally to Totty. 'Two K's,' said Totty, and tittered uncontrollably. I spelt it to Wally; he looked surprised, and said, 'Oh ta.' I had pushed myself, but it was done now. . . . 'When I was a marstah in Sheerness,' rasped Totty under his breath, in Bummer's waspish voice; Wally snickered mechanically, caught the teacher's eye, coughed and coloured and smiled. The teacher smiled back and shook her head, I saw him fleeting down the touchline – 'played Walters!' . . . 'Coomin' to the pitchers, 'Utch? New serial, exploits o' summat or other.' Elaine! I felt more out of it than ever.

Two days later, after a slab of Algebra, x plus 6 plus y squared, we the Welsh class stumped out, passing Rogers on his purposeful way to the lab, aglow with Science. I was downcast. 'Dysgwch y pedair gradd cymhariaeth, learn the four degrees of comparison.' The Boss was just leaving us to it, when he hesitated and turned. 'George Williams,' he said, 'tyd hefo fi am funud, come with me.' I looked up, surprised: he had never said my name before, and a summons to his study was a serious matter. I looked at the others and followed, was it my Chemistry? – by then I was inside. He spoke in English. 'Miss Cooke,' he said, 'hass made a proposall to me. It iss irregular but with your Welsh so good coming from a Welsh home you are to move over to French.'

I stared at him. Miss Cooke had never spoken a direct word to me, had he confused me with another pupil? It was like being told, standing in the Coronation crowd, that royalty has expressed approval of the way you wave and wants you inside the Palace to wave there. 'Go along.' I turned. 'Not back to the Welsh,' he said, 'to Form One.' 'Yes sir,' I remembered Mam. 'Excuse me sir, will I have to get books?' 'Only one.' I sleep-walked to Form One, and heard a trumpet-call, 'Nous avons, Vous avez, Ils ont!' The class repeated it after her. Waiting for the high parrot voices to finish, I knew that my life had begun.

I knocked and entered, sensing with a nervous thrill that to the pupils my advent was a surprise. I had never seen Miss Cooke standing before a class; she was rubbing out on the blackboard, great trenchant sweeps. 'Please, Miss—' 'I know,' she said without turning her head, 'sit down.' She tossed me a new exercise-book; I caught it and sat. 'Le Roi Georges Cinq,' she wrote in a large flowing hand, 'le drapeau du roi, les drapeaux des rois, le président Monsieur Poincaré.' She chalked the accents like proud combs on cockerels; then she spoke each word and the class intoned after her. In 'drapeau', to make the girls blush, Totty and Co brought out the 'po' sound as weighted as they dared, but it did not distract me; I was alone, for the first time, with the blackboard-face of France.

I thought, this is not past like Latin, I have heard this spoken by the nuns; it is being spoken now by thousands of people, and I am going to speak it too. Miss Cooke said ' "Le roi" singular and "les rois" plural are pronounced the same, but you can *feel* the s on the end if you listen to the "les".' She could teach. My hand shot up, I did not care if I was showing off – I was – I desperately wanted her to know that she would have no regrets. 'Please, Miss—', 'please, Miss Cooke,' she interrupted, 'please, Miss Cooke,' I said undeterred, 'why does the plural of "roi" end in s and of "drapeau" in x?' 'S is the usual form but there are exceptions, copy them from Millie Tyrer and don't ask any more questions until you have caught up, it impedes the lesson.' I did not take it as a snub, I had done what I wanted to do.

'Now,' she said, taking the stance I remembered, one booted foot over the other, hands tucked under arms, 'the word "fille", meaning both "girl" and "daughter", is not easy for English people.' I saw Totty look blank, and frown; Wally was baffled. But, I thought, dribbling down a French touchline out of his reach – in Welsh 'merch' means the same two things, what is difficult about it? My promotion was going to my head. Five minutes later I discovered that in French every stick and stone was either masculine or feminine, and that adjectives followed nouns and changed gender, but so did they in Welsh, pen mawr,[3] llwy fawr![4] After dinner I doubled back into the classroom, wrote 'G. Wms, French,' and spent thirty fleeting minutes copying Millie Tyrer's notes. The recurrent virile thud of the football was no longer a reproach; with its every smack I was smacking back, with a stroke of the pen. 'Le pont, the bridge.' I hardly had to write that, 'pont' is the Welsh for bridge, as 'ffenestr' is for window.

The afternoon walk was the shortest yet, and the least hungry; the day's notes in my hand, in the crisp sun, I bookwormed my way home. I spoke the words aloud, 'René est un garçon, Louise est une petite fille.' People smiled but I did not care. In the twilight of Whitford, a child was crossing the bridge with her mother. 'Louise,' I said to the Welsh air, 'la fille de Madame Pascal, est sur le pont.' 'Any news?' said Mam. 'Oh, this tastes good,' I said, 'as good as school dinner – yes, Miss Cooke is teaching me French.' She looked at me, puzzled. 'The cook teaching you French?' '*Miss* Cooke,' I mumbled between Rolly and Polly, 'the one who talks as if she was a man.' 'Is she going to be like that Mr Hedges? We don't want your father putting her in her place with his soft words, French, well . . .' 'It's like Welsh, only different.' 'He went there in that ship of his, do you want some more?' 'Merci, Mam,' I said, 'je suis le fils de Madame Williams.' 'Well,' said Mam, 'you are a quick one, how much was your book?'

Miss Cooke and I were to exchange no personal word, even of small talk, for several years; but the unspoken challenge was taken on, from a dynamo of thirty-four to a tyro of eleven. That night I worked late, I was determined to catch up, and in miraculous time. The next day I rose in the half-dark with more alacrity, and the winter sun seemed to come up minutes earlier, with a cold but gladdening eye. Brain refreshed, I stepped out past Maen Achwyfan

of the wise worn face, and found all the words which I had crammed last night higgledy-piggledy into a drawer of memory, now neatly marshalled, 'J'ai un oeil, j'ai deux yeux. . . .' As I dipped into Whitford, 7.55 to the second, it came upon me that 'cheval' was the same as 'ceffyl' (pronounced keffil) which is Welsh for horse, and that 'cavalier' had to do with both. 'The Keffileers and the Roundheads,' I said to the hedgerows, exhilarated at my discovery: I should have liked Miss Cooke to know of it. Ever after, to me a 'Chevalier de la Légion d'Honneur' was to be an old Welsh farm-hand with a red ribbon in his lapel. Striding past Tŷ Celyn, with a French circumflex, I was aglow with new knowledge, a walking dictionary and proud of it.

I was careful not to exasperate with questions, but by the end of the following week I had caught up. Two weeks later, February weather, with boys running to clamp hands on the hot pipes between lessons, I met Miss Cooke who said, 'See here, Williams, what time d'you leave home?' 'Half-past seven, Miss Cooke.' 'I'm sure your mother would agree that before school you could do with a cup of hot cocoa.' I did not know cocoa. 'You know where my lodgings are?' 'Yes, Miss Cooke.' I didn't, but dared not contradict her. 'Right, nip over before school tomorrow.' I did not tell Mam, I thought I would try the cocoa first.

Next morning I put on a spurt, it would not do to take the cocoa and then be late for prayers, and stole up to her lodgings, opposite the school: the Tudor-beamed pebble-splashed villa of a preacher. As I opened the gate, a couple of girls looked at me curiously. I blushed, but could be collecting a book, tried to unblush, but they had gone. 'In there,' said a mild Welsh matron, and disappeared. I looked pityingly after her, fancy being Miss Cooke's landlady: 'Mrs Evans, you've dusted my table abominably, four a.m. and not yet light but by jingo I'll have you out of bed before you can say Jack Robinson. . . .' On the corner of the plush table-cloth, on a spotless napkin, a large steaming cup. I perched on the edge of a chair, sipped, and peered surreptitiously round.

It was a clean drab room overrun by an alien personality, as if the coloured-glass doors facing Holywell Mountain had been opened for sixty seconds to a ninety-mile-an-hour hurricane and then calvinistically sealed. There were the remains of a wolfed breakfast: scattered crumbs, an egg-cup on its side and half a cup of tea slopped into the saucer, not by a shaking hand but through an abstracted eye. The preacher's library, as safe behind the glass of the bookcase as the Highland cattle behind theirs, stood marshalled dogma shoulder to dogma, but the hurricane had got at the rest of the room and strewn it with literary débris; yet it was not disorder, but rather order of a tempestuous kind. Stray sheets, splashed with memoranda, spilled over an aspidistra; on the sideboard, a French periodical, its back broken and pages pinned back and scored in red, lay next to a book called Voltaire, both hemmed between a framed Methodist and a cast-iron sheep, while a volumi-nous newspaper was spreadeagled over the arm-chair: *The Observer*, the name was new to me. On the floor, a pile of exercise-books corrected, slapped-to and flung down like shelled pods, and on the sideboard, next to an umpire's whistle (hockey), another pile open, one on top of the other, meekly awaiting the eviscerant pencil ('rubbish!', 'v. gd.', 'fiddlesticks!', 'well tried'). Blown open on to chair-arm and ledge, every variety of text-book, wedged with book-marks: Latin, French and even Spanish. This last puzzled me, the idea of Miss Cooke being her own pupil was beyond my grasp. Never once at this daily ritual did I see her. Mam approved, 'You said thank you?' 'Mind she doesn't poison you,' said Dad, 'these suffragettes are very absent-minded, she might slip something in out of that Lab, watch out!'

Miss Cooke's next move came on a morning of sleet and hail. 'See here, Williams,' she said, braking amid the traffic of the Central Hall, 'my family are to do with leather, draw your foot on this.' I unfolded a section of brown paper, took it to the lavatories and drew my foot. A week later, next to cocoa, lay an opened parcel; two boots set fair and square for rain and snow, seven-league Yorkshire leather built strip by strip for an infant Hercules. They made what I had on look like a couple of wrinkled old country ladies, but pride insisted that I wear these one more day, to prove that their case was not too parlous. Also, would it not be better tactics to arrive home with the new ones under my arm? I was right. 'What is the parcel?' said Mam. I explained, between mouthfuls. 'Oh,' she said, with a quick glance at my feet, which straight from five miles of muddy highway looked their worst. I knew her unspoken dread of her children going barefoot, to her the mark of destitution. 'Has somebody said anything?' 'Oh no,' I said, chewing, 'Miss Cooke said what good boots mine were, but her family make them, the place is full of boots, they don't know what to do with them.' After my tea I changed into the new ones and stamped around. They caressed my ankles with the gentle touch of the strong; on Sunday I had to change into them for Dad. 'Dear Miss Cooke,' he wrote in his elegant hand, in the ruled book he used for his bets, 'We are very thank-full to you for taking interest' – the pen made a fastidious circle as he pondered the right word – 'in our son's well-fare, and let us hope he will be a credit to us all' – a final hover while formality was decided on, plus abbreviation – 'we remain Yrs. Obediently R. and M. Wms.' 'Poll,' he said, licking the envelope with a flourish, 'Dic[5] goes to the top of the class!'

GLOSSARY
1 *Flint*: a town in North Wales.
2 *Savonarola*: an Italian religious reformer (1452–98).
3 *pen mawr*: big head (or it can mean 'the top of the hill' or 'head of the valley').
4 *llwy fawr*: big spoon. In Welsh, like French, nouns are masculine or feminine and this affects the adjectives: here 'mawr' ('big') has the masculine form and 'fawr' ('big') the feminine.
5 *Dic*: the author's father.

SUGGESTIONS FOR WRITING AND DISCUSSION

1 *What impression do you get of the author from the first section of this extract? (For instance, does he seem too keen? A little smug? Admirably ambitious? Brainy and lively? Determined to get on? Ashamed of being Welsh?)*
2 *Comment on his attitude towards language. (For instance, consider his thoughts about Welsh, English and French.)*
3 *How does the author manage to convey his delight in learning?*
4 *Describe the impression you get of Miss Cooke.*
5 *Write about the school subjects you enjoy most and least and explain why.*
6 *'Stray sheets splashed with memoranda ...'. Read again how Emlyn Williams describes Miss Cooke's room. Describe a room you know (or could imagine) and show how it reflects – somehow – the personality of its owner.*
7 *'These suffragettes are very absent-minded ...' Why do you think George's father calls Miss Cooke a suffragette? What did the suffragettes achieve in 1915 (the year George would have been ten)? Find out what you can and write a short piece on one of the following: Hannah Mitchell, Vera Brittain, Emily Pankhurst, Elizabeth Garrett Anderson.*
8 *Give your impression of George's family from the details in the extract. In what ways do you think life has changed for a working-class family between 1915 and the present day?*

FURTHER READING

George Emlyn Williams (Hamish Hamilton)
The Corn Is Green Emlyn Williams (Heinemann Educational Books)

SALMAN RUSHDIE

Salman Rushdie was born in Bombay in 1947 and now lives in London. His novel *Midnight's Children* is a complex and original account of human and political life in India following independence. Its hero, Saleem Sinai, was born at midnight at the beginning of India's independence on 15 August 1947. The novel won the Booker Prize in 1981. Since then, Rushdie has published two other novels, *Shame* and *Grimus*.

THE MUTILATIONS OF SALEEM

The first mutilation of Saleem Sinai, which was rapidly followed by the second, took place one Wednesday early in 1958 – the Wednesday of the much-anticipated Social – under the auspices of the Anglo-Scottish Education Society. That is, it happened at school.

Saleem's assailant: handsome, frenetic, with a barbarian's shaggy moustache: I present the leaping, hair-tearing figure of Mr Emil Zagallo, who taught us geography and gymnastics, and who, that morning, unintentionally precipitated the crisis of my life. Zagallo claimed to be Peruvian, and was fond of calling us jungle-Indians, bead-lovers; he hung a print of a stern, sweaty soldier in a pointy tin hat and metal pantaloons above his blackboard and had a way of stabbing a finger at it in times of stress and shouting, 'You see heem, you savages? Thees man eez civilization! You show heem respect: he's got a *sword*!' And he'd swish his cane through the stone-walled air. We called him Pagal-Zagal, crazy Zagallo, because for all his talk of llamas and conquistadores and the Pacific Ocean we knew, with the absolute certainty of rumour, that he'd been born in a Mazagaon[1] tenement and his Goanese[2] mother had been abandoned by a decamped shipping agent; so he was not only an 'Anglo'[3] but probably a bastard as well. Knowing this, we understood why Zagallo affected his Latin accent, and also why he was always in a fury, why he beat his fists against the stone walls of the classroom; but the knowledge didn't stop us being afraid. And this Wednesday morning, we knew we were in for trouble, because Optional Cathedral had been cancelled.

The Wednesday morning double period was Zagallo's geography class; but only idiots and boys with bigoted parents attended it, because it was also the time when we could choose to troop off to St Thomas's Cathedral in crocodile formation, a long line of boys of every conceivable religious denomination, escaping from school into the bosom of the Christians' considerately optional God. It drove Zagallo wild, but he was helpless; today, however, there was a dark glint in his eye, because the Croaker (that is to say, Mr Crusoe the headmaster) had announced at morning Assembly that Cathedral was cancelled. In a bare, scraped voice emerging from his face of an anaesthetized frog, he sentenced us to double geography and Pagal-Zagal, taking us all by surprise, because we hadn't realized that God was permitted to exercise an option, too. Glumly we trooped into Zagallo's lair; one of the poor idiots whose parents never allowed them to go to Cathedral whispered viciously into my ear, 'You jus' wait: he'll really get you guys today.'

Padma:[4] he really did.

Seated gloomily in class: Glandy Keith Colaco, Fat Perce Fishwala, Jimmy Kapadia the scholarship boy whose father was a taxi-driver, Hairoil Sabarmati, Sonny Ibrahim, Cyrus-the-great and I. Others, too, but there's no time now, because with eyes narrowing in delight, crazy Zagallo is calling us to order.

'Human geography,' Zagallo announces. 'Thees ees *what*? Kapadia?'

'Please sir don't know sir.' Hands fly into the air – five belong to church-banned idiots, the sixth inevitably to Cyrus-the-great. But Zagallo is out for blood today: the godly are going to suffer. 'Feelth from the jongle,' he buffets Jimmy Kapadia, then begins to twist an ear casually, 'Stay in class sometimes and find out!'

'Ow ow ow yes sir sorry sir . . .' Six hands are waving but Jimmy's ear is in danger of coming off. Heroism gets the better of me . . . 'Sir please stop sir he has a heart condition sir!' Which is true; but the truth is dangerous, because now Zagallo is rounding on me: 'So, a leetle arguer, ees eet?' And I am being led by my hair to the front of the class. Under the relieved eyes of my fellow-pupils – *thank God it's him not us* – I writhe in agony beneath imprisoned tufts.

'So answer the question. You know what ees human geography?'

Pain fills my head, obliterating all notions of telepathic cheatery: 'Aiee sir no sir ouch!'

. . . And now it is possible to observe a joke descending on Zagallo, a joke pulling his face apart into the simulacrum of a smile; it is possible to watch his hand darting forward, thumb-and-forefinger extended; to note how thumb-and-forefinger close around the tip of my nose and pull downwards . . . where the nose leads, the head must follow, and finally the nose is hanging down and my eyes are obliged to stare damply at Zagallo's sandalled feet with their dirty toenails while Zagallo unleashes his wit.

'See, boys – you see what we have here? Regard, please, the heedeous face of thees primitive creature. It reminds you of?'

And the eager responses: 'Sir the devil sir.' 'Please sir one cousin of mine!' 'No sir a vegetable sir I don't know which.' Until Zagallo, shouting above the tumult, 'Silence! Sons of baboons! Thees object here' – a tug on my nose – '*thees* is human geography!'

'How sir where sir what sir?'

Zagallo is laughing now. 'You don't see?' he guffaws. 'In the face of thees ugly ape you don't see the whole map of *India*?'

'Yes sir no sir you show us sir!'

'See here – the Deccan peninsula hanging down!' Again ouchmynose.

'Sir sir if that's the map of India what are the stains sir?' It is Glandy Keith Colaco feeling bold. Sniggers, titters from my fellows. And Zagallo, taking the question in his stride: 'These stains,' he cries, 'are Pakistan! Thees birthmark on the right ear is the East Wing; and thees horrible stained left cheek, the West! Remember, stupid boys: Pakistan ees a stain on the face of India!'

'Ho ho,' the class laughs. 'Absolute master joke, sir!'

But now my nose has had enough; staging its own, unprompted revolt against the grasping thumb-and-forefinger, it unleashes a weapon of its own . . . a large blob of shining goo emerges from the left nostril, to plop into Mr Zagallo's palm. Fat Perce Fishwala yells, 'Lookit that, sir! The drip from his nose, sir! Is that supposed to be *Ceylon*?'

His palm smeared with goo, Zagallo loses his jokey mood. 'Animal,' he curses me. 'You see what you do?' Zagallo's hand releases my nose; returns to hair. Nasal refuse is wiped into my neatly parted locks. And now, once again, my hair is seized; once again, the hand is pulling . . . but upward now, and my head has jerked upright, my feet are moving on to tiptoe, and Zagallo, 'What are you? Tell me what you are!'

'Sir an animal sir!'

The hand pulls harder higher. 'Again.' Standing on my toenails now, I yelp: 'Aiee sir an animal an animal please sir aiee!'

And still harder and still higher . . . 'Once more!' But suddenly it ends; my feet are flat on the ground again; and the class has fallen into a deathly hush.

'Sir,' Sonny Ibrahim is saying, 'you pulled his hair out, sir.'

And now the cacophony: 'Look sir, blood.' 'He's bleeding sir.' 'Please sir shall I take him to the nurse?'

Mr Zagallo stood like a statue with a clump of my hair in his fist. While I – too shocked to feel any pain – felt the patch on my head where Mr Zagallo had created a monkish tonsure, a circle where hair would never grow again, and realized that the curse of my birth, which connected me to my country, had managed to find yet one more unexpected expression of itself.

Two days later, Croaker Crusoe announced that, unfortunately, Mr Emil Zagallo was leaving the staff for personal reasons; but I knew what the reasons were. My uprooted hairs had stuck to his hands, like bloodstains that wouldn't wash out, and nobody wants a teacher with hair on his palms. 'The first sign of madness,' as Glandy Keith was fond of saying, 'and the second sign is looking for them.'

Zagallo's legacy: a monk's tonsure; and, worse than that, a whole set of new taunts, which my classmates flung at me while we waited for school buses to take us home to get dressed for the Social: 'Snotnose is a bal-die!' and, 'Sniffer's got a map-face!' When Cyrus arrived in the bus-queue, I tried to turn the crowd against him, by attempting to set up a chant of 'Cyrus-the-great, Born on a plate, In nineteen hundred and forty-eight,' but nobody took up the offer.

So we come to the events of the Cathedral School Social. At which bullies became instruments of destiny, and fingers were transmuted into fountains, and Masha Miovic, the legendary breast-stroker, fell into a dead faint . . . I arrived at the Social with the nurse's bandage still on my head. I was late, because it hadn't been easy to persuade my mother to let me come; so by the time I stepped into the Assembly Hall, beneath streamers and balloons and the professionally suspicious gazes of bony female chaperons, all the best girls were already box-stepping and Mexican-Hatting with absurdly smug partners. Naturally, the prefects had the pick of the ladies; I watched them with passionate envy, Guzder and Joshi and Stevenson and Rushdie and Talyarkhan and Tayabali and Jussawalla and Waglé and King; I tried butting in on them during excuse-mes but when they saw my bandage and my cucumber of a nose and the stains on my face they just laughed and turned their backs ... hatred burgeoning in my bosom, I ate potato chips and drank Bubble-Up and Vimto and told myself, 'Those jerks; if they knew who I was they'd get out of my way pretty damn quick!' But still the fear of revealing my true nature was stronger than my somewhat abstract desire for the whirling European girls.

'Hey, Saleem isn't it? Hey, man, what happened to you?' I was dragged out of my bitter, solitary reverie (even Sonny had someone to dance with; but then, he had his forcep-hollows, and he didn't wear underpants – there were reasons for his attractiveness) by a voice behind my left shoulder, a low, throaty voice, full of promises – but also of menaces. A girl's voice. I turned with a sort of jump and found myself staring at a vision with golden hair and a prominent and famous chest ... my God, she was fourteen years old, why was she talking to me? ... 'My name is Masha Miovic,' the vision said, 'I've met your sister.'

Of course! The Monkey's heroines, the swimmers from Walsingham School, would certainly know the Schools champion breast-stroker! ... 'I know ...' I stuttered, 'I know your name.'

'And I know yours,' she straightened my tie, 'so that's fair.' Over her shoulder, I saw Glandy Keith and Fat Perce watching us in drooling paroxysms of envy. I straightened my back and pushed out my shoulders. Masha Miovic asked again about my bandage. 'It's nothing,' I said in what I hoped was a deep voice. 'A sporting accident.' And then, working feverishly to hold my voice steady, 'Would you like to ... to dance?'

'Okay,' said Masha Miovic. 'But don't try any smooching.'

Saleem takes the floor with Masha Miovic, swearing not to smooch. Saleem and Masha, doing the Mexican Hat; Masha and Saleem, box-stepping with the best of them! I allow my face to adopt a superior expression; you see, you don't have to be a prefect to get a girl! ... The dance ended; and, still on top of my wave of elation, I said, 'Would you care for a stroll, you know, in the quad?'

Masha Miovic smiling privately. 'Well, yah, just for a sec; but hands off, okay?'

Hands off, Saleem swears. Saleem and Masha, taking the air ... man, this is fine. This is the life. Goodbye Evie, hello breast-stroke ... Glandy Keith Colaco and Fat Perce Fishwala step out of the shadows of the quadrangle. They are giggling: 'Hee hee.' Masha Miovic looks puzzled as they block our path. 'Hoo hoo,' Fat Perce says, 'Masha, hoo hoo. Some date you got there.' And I, 'Shut up, you.' Whereupon Glandy Keith, 'You wanna know how he got his war-wound, Mashy?' And Fat Perce, 'Hee hoo ha.' Masha says, 'Don't be *crude*; he got it in a sporting accident!' Fat Perce and Glandy Keith are almost falling over with mirth; then Fishwala reveals all. 'Zagallo pulled his hair out in class!' Hee hoo. And Keith, 'Snotnose is a bal-die!' And both together, 'Sniffer's got a map-face!' There is puzzlement on Masha Miovic's face. And something more, some budding spirit of sexual mischief ... 'Saleem, they're being so rude about you!'

'Yes,' I say, 'ignore them.' I try to edge her away. But she goes on, 'You aren't going to let them get away with it?' There are beads of excitement on her upper lip; her tongue is in the corner of her mouth; the eyes of Masha Miovic say, *What are you? A man or a mouse?* . . . and under the spell of the champion breast-stroker, something else floats into my head: the image of two irresistible knees; and now I am rushing at Colaco and Fishwala; while they are distracted by giggles, my knee drives into Glandy's groin; before he's dropped, a similar genuflection has laid Fat Perce low. I turn to my mistress; she applauds, softly. 'Hey man, pretty good.'

But now my moment has passed; and Fat Perce is picking himself up, and Glandy Keith is already moving towards me . . . abandoning all pretence of manhood, I turn and run. And the two bullies are after me and behind them comes Masha Miovic calling, 'Where are you running, little hero?' But there's no time for her now, mustn't let them get me, into the nearest classroom and try and shut the door, but Fat Perce's foot is in the way and now the two of them are inside too and I dash at the door, I grab it with my right hand, trying to force it open, *get out if you can*, they are pushing the door shut, but I'm pulling with the strength of my fear, I have it open a few inches, my hand curls around it, and now Fat Perce slams all his weight against the door and it shuts too fast for me to get my hand out of the way and it's shut. A thud. And outside, Masha Miovic arrives and looks down at the floor; and sees the top third of my middle finger lying there like a lump of well-chewed bubble-gum. This was the point at which she fainted.

No pain. Everything very far away. Fat Perce and Glandy Keith fleeing, to get help or to hide. I look at my hand out of pure curiosity. My finger has become a fountain: red liquid spurts out to the rhythm of my heart-beat. Never knew a finger held so much blood. Pretty. Now here's nurse, don't worry, nurse. Only a scratch. *Your parents are being phoned; Mr Crusoe is getting his car keys.* Nurse is putting a great wad of cotton-wool over the stump. Filling up like red candy-floss. And now Crusoe. Get in the car, Saleem, your mother is going straight to the hospital. Yes sir. And the bit, has anybody got the *bit*? Yes headmaster here it is. Thank you nurse. Probably no use but you never know. Hold this while I drive, Saleem . . . and holding up my severed finger-tip in my unmutilated left hand, I am driven to the Breach Candy Hospital through the echoing streets of night.

At the hospital: white walls stretchers everyone talking at once. Words pour around me like fountains. 'O God preserve us, my little piece-of-the-moon, what have they done to you?' To which old Crusoe, 'Heh heh. Mrs Sinai. Accidents will happen. Boys will be.' But my mother, enraged, 'What kind of school? Mr Caruso? I'm here with my son's finger in pieces and you tell me. Not good enough. No, sir.' And now, while Crusoe, 'Actually the name's – like Robinson, you know – heh heh,' the doctor is approaching and a question is being asked, whose answer will change the world.

'Mrs Sinai, your blood group, please? The boy has lost blood. A transfusion may be necessary.' And Amina: 'I am A; but my husband, O.' And now she is crying, breaking down, and still the doctor, 'Ah; in that case, are you aware of your son's . . .' But she, the doctor's daughter, must admit she cannot answer the question: Alpha or Omega? 'Well in that case a very quick test; but on the subject of rhesus?' My mother, through her tears: 'Both my husband and I, rhesus positive.' And the doctor, 'Well, good, that at least.'

But when I am on the operating table – 'Just sit there, son, I'll give you a local anaesthetic, no, madam, he's in shock, total anaesthesia would be impossible, all right son, just hold your finger up and still, help him nurse, and it'll be over in a jiffy' – while the surgeon is sewing up the stump and performing the miracle of transplanting the roots of the nail, all of a sudden there's a fluster in the background, a million miles away, and 'Have you got a second Mrs Sinai' and I can't hear properly . . . words float across the infinite distance . . . Mrs Sinai, you are sure? O and A? A and O? And rhesus positive, both of you? Heterozygous or homozygous? No, there must be some mistake, how can he be . . . I'm sorry, absolutely clear . . . negative . . . and neither A nor . . . excuse me, Madam, but is he your . . . not adopted or . . . The hospital nurse interposes herself between me and the miles-away chatter, but it's no good, because now my mother is shrieking, 'But of course you must believe me, doctor, my God, *of course he is our son!*'

GLOSSARY
1 *Mazagaon*: Mazagao is a town in north Brazil.
2 *Goanese*: Goa is on the west coast of India. Formerly a Portuguese possession, it is now part of India.
3 *'Anglo'*: of mixed English and Indian descent.
4 *Padma*: the girl to whom the narrator is telling the story.

SUGGESTIONS FOR WRITING AND DISCUSSION

1 *Write a description of Mr Zagallo.*
2 *What impression do you get of the school Saleem attended?*
3 *Do you think the author is successful in describing the way adolescent pupils behave?*
4 *What dreadful discovery about Saleem does this extract lead up to?*
5 *Comment on the style in which this extract is written (the irreverent tone; his use of the present tense; his imitation of people's accents; his direct appeal to the reader).*
6 *Say whether or not you think this extract is comic and give reasons.*
7 *Write a story about an accident that occurs at school.*
8 *Write a story about someone going to a dance or disco for the first time.*

FURTHER READING

Midnight's Children Salman Rushdie (Cape)
Shame Salman Rushdie (Cape)
Grimus Salman Rushdie (Panther)

EDNA O'BRIEN

Edna O'Brien was born in County Clare, Ireland. She now lives in London. She has written novels, short stories and plays for the stage and television. Her early work was striking because of the freshness of detail and the originality with which she described Irish life. The themes of her fiction are sexual love and the pursuit of fulfilment from a woman's point of view. *The Country Girls* is the first of three novels (the other two are *The Lonely Girl* and *Girls in Their Married Bliss*) which follow the lives of Caithleen and Baba. In *The Country Girls* Caithleen has an unhappy affair with a married man (Mr Gentleman).

LAST DAY OF CHILDHOOD

We set out for the town hall just before seven. Mr Brennan was not home, so we left the table set and when Martha[1] was upstairs getting ready I put a damp napkin round his plate of sandwiches. I was sorry for Mr Brennan. He worked hard and he had an ulcer.

Declan[2] went on ahead. He thought it was cissyish to walk with girls.

The sun was going down and it made a fire in the western part of the sky. Running out from the fire, there were pathways of colour, not red like the sun, but a warm, flushed pink. The sky above it was a naked blue, and higher still, over our heads, great eiderdowns of clouds sailed serenely by. Heaven was up there. I knew no one in Heaven. Except old women in the village who had died, but no one belonging to me.

'My mammy is the best-looking woman round here,' Baba said. In fact I thought my mother was; with her round, pale, heart-breaking face and her grey, trusting eyes; but I didn't say so because I was staying in their house. Martha did look lovely. The setting sun, or maybe it was the coral necklace, gave her eyes a mysterious orange glow.

'BBBIP BBBIP,' said Hickey[3] as he cycled past us. I was always sorry for Hickey's bicycle. I expected it to collapse under his weight. The tyres looked flat. He was carrying a can of milk on the handlebar and a rush basket with a live hen clucking in it. Probably for Mrs O'Shea in the Greyhound Hotel. Hickey always treated his friends when Mama was away. I supposed Mama had the chickens counted, but Hickey could say the fox came. The foxes were always coming into the yard in broad daylight and carrying off a hen or a turkey.

In front of us, like specks of brown dust, the hordes of midges were humming to themselves under the trees and my ears were itchy after we had passed through that part of the road near the forge, where there was a grove of beech trees.

'Hurry,' said Martha, and I took longer steps. She wanted seats in the front row. Important people sat there. The doctor's wife and Mr Gentleman and the Connor girls. The Connor girls were Protestants but well thought of. They passed us just then in their station-wagon and hooted. It was their way of saying hello. We nodded back to them. There were two alsatians in the back of the car and I was glad they hadn't offered us a lift. I was afraid of alsatians. The Connor girls had a sign on their gate which said 'Beware of Dogs'. They spoke in haughty accents, they rode horses and followed the Hunt in winter-time. When they went to race meetings they had walking-sticks that they could sit on. They never spoke to me, but Martha was invited there for afternoon tea once a year. In the summertime.

We mounted the great flight of concrete steps and went into the porch that led to the town hall. There was a fat woman in the ticket office and we could see only the top half of her. She was wearing a puce dress that had millions of sequins stitched on to it. There were crusts of mascara on her lashes, and her hair was dyed puce to match her dress. It was fascinating to watch the sequins shining as if they were moving on the bodice of her dress.

'Her bubs are dancing,' Baba said and we both sniggered. We were sniggering as we held the double doors for Martha to enter. Martha liked to make an entrance.

'Children, stop laughing,' she said, as if we didn't belong to her.

An actor with pancake make-up beamed at us and went on ahead to find our seats. Martha had given him three blue tickets.

The country boys in the back of the hall whistled as we came in. It was their habit to stand there and pass remarks about the girls as they came in, and then laugh, or whistle if the girl was pretty. They were in their old clothes but most of them probably had their Sunday shoes on, and there was a strong smell of hair oil.

'Uncouth,' Martha said under her breath. It was her favourite word for most of her husband's customers. There was one nice boy who smiled at me, he had black curly hair and a red, happy face. I knew he was on the hurley[4] team.

We were sitting in the front row. Martha sat next to the eldest Connor girl, Baba next to her, and I was on the outside. Mr Gentleman was farther in, near the younger Connor girl. I saw the back of his neck and the top of his collar before I sat down. I was glad to know that he was there.

The hall was almost dark. Curtains of black cloth had been put over the windows and pinned to the window-frames at the four corners. The light from the six oil-lamps at the front of the stage barely showed people to their seats. Two of the lamps smoked and the globes were black.

I looked back to see if there was any sign of Hickey. I looked through the rows of chairs, then along the rows of stools behind the chairs, and farther back still I searched with my eyes along the planks that were laid on porter barrels. He was at the end of the last row of planks with Maisie next to him. The cheapest seats. They were laughing. The back of the hall was full of girls laughing. Girls with curly hair, girls with shiny black coils of it, like bunches of elderberries, falling on to their shoulders, girls with moist blackberry eyes; smirking and talking and waiting. Miss Moriarty was two rows behind us and she bowed lightly to acknowledge that she saw me. Jack Holland was writing into a notebook.

A bell gonged and the dusty grey curtain was drawn slowly back. It got stuck half-way. The boys at the back booed. I could see the actor with the pancake make-up pulling a string from the wings of the stage and finally he came out and pushed the curtain back with his hands. The crowd cheered.

On stage were four girls in cerise blouses, black frilly pants, and black hard hats. They had canes under their arms and they tap-danced. I wished that Mama were there. In all the excitement I hadn't thought of her for over an hour. She would have enjoyed it especially when she heard about the scholarship.[5]

The girls danced off, two to the right and two to the left, and then a man carrying a banjo came on and sang sad songs. He could turn his two eyes inwards and when he did everyone laughed.

After that came a laughing sketch where two clowns got in and out of boxes and then the woman in the puce dress sang 'Courting in the Kitchen'. She waved to the audience to join in with her and towards the end they did. She was awful.

'And now, ladies and gentlemen, there will be a short interval, during which time we will sell tickets that will be raffled immediately before the play. And the play, as you probably know, is the one and only, the heart-warming, tear-making *East Lynne*,'[6] said the man with the pancake make-up.

I had no money but Martha bought me four tickets.

'If you win it's mine,' said Baba. Mr Gentleman passed his packet of cigarettes all along the front row. Martha took one and leaned forward to thank him. Baba and I ate Turkish Delight.

When the tickets were sold the actor came down and stood under the oil-lamps; he put the duplicate ones into a big hat and looked around for someone to draw the winning numbers. Children were usually picked to do this, as they were supposed to be honest. He looked down the hall and then he looked at Baba and me and he chose us. We stood up and faced the audience and she picked the first number and I picked the next one. He called out the winning numbers. He called them three times, but nothing happened. You could hear a pin drop. He said them once more and he was just on the point of asking us to draw two more tickets when there came a shout from the back of the hall.

'Here, down here,' people said.

'Now you must come forward and show your tickets.' People liked winning but they were ashamed to come up and collect the prizes. At last they shuffled out from among the standing crowd and the two winners came hesitantly up the passage. One was an albino and the other was a young boy. They showed their tickets, collected their ten shillings each, and went back in a half-run to the darkness at the end of the hall.

'And how about a little song from our two charming friends here?' he said, putting a hand on each of our shoulders.

'Yes,' said Baba who was always looking for an excuse to show off her clear, light, early-morning voice. She began: 'As I was going one morning, 'twas in the month of May, a mother and her daughter I spied along the way,' and I opened and closed my mouth to pretend that I was singing too. But she stopped all of a sudden and nudged me to carry on, and there I was, seen by everyone in the hall with my mouth wide open as if I had lockjaw. I blushed and faded back to my seat and Baba went on with her song. 'Witch,' I said, under my breath.

East Lynne began. There was dead silence everywhere, except for voices on the stage.

Then I heard noise in the back of the hall, and shuffling as if someone had fainted. A flashlamp travelled up along the passage and as it came level with us I saw that it was Mr Brennan.

'Jesus, it's about the chicken,' Baba said to her mother, as Mr Brennan called Martha out. He crossed over, stooping so as not to be in the way of the stage and he whispered to Mr Gentleman. Both of them went out. I heard the door being shut noisily and I was glad that they were gone. The play was so good, I didn't want to miss a line.

But the door was opened again and the beam of the flashlamp came up along the hall. A thought struck me that they wanted me and then I put it aside again. But it was me. Mr Brennan tapped me on the shoulder and whispered, 'Caithleen love, I want you a minute.' My shoes creaked as I went down the hall on tip-toe. I expected it was something about my father.

Outside in the porch they were all talking – Martha and the parish priest, and Mr Gentleman and the solicitor and Hickey. Hickey had his back to me and Martha was crying. It was Mr Gentleman who told me.

'Your mother, Caithleen, she's had a little accident'; he spoke slowly and gravely and his voice was unsteady.

'What kind of an accident?' I asked, staring wildly at all the faces. Martha was suffocating into her handkerchief.

'A little accident,' Mr Gentleman said, again, and the parish priest repeated it.

'Where is she?' I asked, quickly, wildly. I wanted to get to her at once. At once. But no one answered.

'Tell me,' I said. My voice was hysterical and then I realized that I was being rude to the parish priest, and I asked again, only more gently.

'Tell her, 'tis better to tell her,' I heard Hickey say behind my back. I turned round to ask him but Mr Brennan shook his head and Hickey blushed under the grey stubble of his two-day beard.

'Take me to Mama,' I begged, as I ran out of the doorway and down the flight of concrete steps. At the last step, someone caught me by the belt of my coat.

'We can't take you yet, not yet, Caithleen,' Mr Gentleman said, and I thought that they were all very cruel, and I couldn't understand why.

'Why? Why? I want to go to her,' I said, trying to escape from his grip. I had so much strength that I could have run the whole five-mile journey to Tintrim.

'For God's sake, tell the girl,' Hickey said.

'Shut up, Hickey,' Mr Brennan shouted, and moved me over to the edge of the kerb where there were several motor-cars. There were people gathering round the motor-cars and everyone was talking and mumbling in the dark. Martha helped me into the back of their car, and just before she slammed the door I heard two voices in the street talking, and one voice said, 'He left five children.'

'Who left five children?' I said to Martha, clutching her by the wrists. I sobbed and said her name and begged her to tell me.

'Tom O'Brien, Caithleen. He's drowned. In his boat, and, and ...' She would rather be struck dumb than tell me, but I knew it by her face.

'And Mama?' I asked. She nodded her poor head and put her arms round me. Mr Brennan got into the front seat just then and started the car.

'She knows,' Martha said to him, between her sobs, but after that I heard nothing, because you hear nothing, nor no one, when your whole body cries and cries for the thing it has lost. Lost. Lost. And yet I could not believe that my mother was gone; and still I knew it was true because I had a feeling of doom and every bit of me was frozen stiff.

'Are we going to Mama?' I said.

'In a while, Caithleen; we have to get something first,' they told me as they helped me out of the car and led me into the Greyhound Hotel. Mrs O'Shea kissed me and put me sitting in one of the big leather armchairs that sloped backwards. The room was full of people. Hickey came over and sat on the arm of my chair. He sat on a white linen antimacassar, but no one cared.

'She's not dead,' I said to him, pleading, beseeching.

'They're missing since five o'clock. They left Tuohey's shop at a quarter to five. Poor Tom O'Brien had two bags of groceries,' Hickey said. Once Hickey said it, it was true. Slowly my knees began to sink from me and everything inside of me was gone. Mr Brennan gave me brandy from a spoon, and then he made me swallow two white pills with a cup of tea.

'She doesn't believe it,' I heard one of the Connor girls say, and then Baba came in and ran over to kiss me.

'I'm sorry about the bloody aul song,' she said.

'Bring the child home,' Jack Holland said, and when I heard him I jumped off the chair, and shouted that I wanted to go to my mother. Mrs O'Shea blessed herself and someone put me sitting down again.

'Caithleen, we're waiting to get news from the barracks,' Mr Gentleman said. He was the only one that could keep me calm.

'I never want to go home again. Never,' I said to him.

'You won't go home, Caithleen,' he said and for a second it seemed that he was going to say, 'Come home to us,' but he didn't. He went over to where Martha was standing beside the sideboard and spoke to her. Then they beckoned to Mr Brennan and he crossed the room to them.

'Where is *he*, Hickey? I don't want to see him.' I was referring to my father.

'You won't see him. He's in hospital in Galway. Passed out when they told him. He was singing in a pub in Portumna when a guard came in to tell him.'

'I'm never going home,' I said to Hickey. His eyes were popping out of his head. He wasn't used to whiskey. Someone had put a tumbler of it in his hand. Everyone was drinking to try and get over the shock. Even Jack Holland took a glass of port wine. The room was thick with cigarette smoke, and I wanted to go out of it, to go out and find Mama, even to go out and find her dead body. It was all too unreal in there and my head was swimming. The ashtrays were overflowing and the room was hot and smoky. Mr Brennan came over to talk to me. He was crying behind his thick lenses. He said my mother was a lady, a true lady; and that everyone loved her.

'Bring me to her,' I asked. I was no longer wild. My strength had been drained from me.

'We're waiting, Caithleen. We're waiting for news from the barracks. I'll go up there now and see if anything's happened. They're searching the river.' He put out his hands, humbly, in a gesture that seemed to say, 'There's nothing any of us can do now.'

'You're staying with us,' he said, as he lifted wild pieces of hair out of my eyes and smoothed them back gently.

'Thank you,' I said, and he went off to the barracks which was a hundred yards up the road. Mr Gentleman went with him.

'That bloody boat was rotten. I always said it,' Hickey said, getting angry with the whole world for not having listened to him.

'Can you come outside, Caithleen? It's confidential,' Jack Holland said as he leaned over the back of my chair. I got up, slowly; and though I cannot remember it, I must have walked across the room to the white door. Most of the paint had been scraped off it. He held it while I went out to the hall. He led me into the back of the hall, where a candle guttered in a saucer. His face was only a shadow. He whispered:

'So help me God, I couldn't do it.'

'Do what, Jack?' I asked. I didn't care. I thought I might get sick or suffocate. The pills and the brandy were gone to my head.

'Give her the money. Jesus, my hands are tied. The old woman owns everything.' The old woman was his mother. She sat on a rocking-chair beside the fire and Jack had to feed her bread and milk because her hands were crippled with rheumatism.

'God, I'd have done anything for your mama; you know that,' and I said that I did.

Upstairs in a bedroom two greyhounds moaned. It was the moan of death. Suddenly I knew that I had to accept the fact that my mother was dead. And I cried as I have never cried at any other time in my life. Jack cried with me and wiped his nose on the sleeve of his coat.

Then the hall door was pushed in, and Mr Brennan came in.

'No news, Caithleen, no news, love. Come on home to bed,' he said, and he called Martha and Baba out of the room.

'We'll try later,' he said to Mr Gentleman. It was a clear, starry night as we walked across the road to the car. We were home in a few minutes and Mr Brennan made me drink hot whiskey and gave me a yellow capsule. Martha helped me take off my clothes, and when I knelt down to say one prayer, I said, 'O God, please bring Mama back to life.' I said it many times but I knew that it was hopeless.

I slept with Baba in one of her nightdresses. Her bed was softer than the one at home. When I turned on my left side she turned too. She put her arm round my stomach and held my hand.

'You're my best friend,' she said in the darkness. And then after a minute she whispered, 'Are you asleep?'

'No.'

'Are you afraid?'

'Afraid of what?'

'That she'll appear,' and when she said it I started to shiver. What is it about death that we cannot bear to have someone who is dead come back to us? I wanted Mama more than anything in the world and yet if the door had opened and she had entered I would have screamed for Martha and Mr Brennan. We heard a noise downstairs, a thud, and we both hid completely under the covers and she said it was death knocks. 'Get Declan,' I said, under the sheet and the blankets.

'No, you go over for him.' But neither of us dared to open the door and go out on the landing. My mother's ghost was waiting for us at the top of the stairs, in a white nightdress.

The pillowslip under me and the white counterpane were wet when I wakened up. Molly wakened me with a cup of tea and toast. She helped me sit up in the bed and fetched my cardigan off the back of a chair. Molly was only two years older than me and yet she fussed over me as if she were my mother.

'Are you sick, love?' she asked. I said that I was hot, and she went off to call Mr Brennan.

'Sir, come here for a second. I want you. I think she has a fever,' and he came and put his hand on my forehead and told Molly to phone the doctor.

They gave me pills all that day and Martha sat in the room and painted her nails and polished them with a little buffer. It was raining, so I couldn't see out the window because it got all fogged up but Martha said it was a terrible day. The phone rang sometime after lunch and Martha kept saying 'Yes, I'll tell her' and 'Too bad' and 'Well, I suppose that's that', and then she came up and told me that they had dragged the great Shannon lake but they hadn't found them; she didn't say that they had given up but I knew they had, and I knew that Mama would never have a grave for me to put flowers on. Somehow she was more dead then than anyone I had ever heard of. I cried again and Martha gave me a sip of wine from her glass and she made me lie back while she read me a story from a magazine. 'Twas a sad story, so I cried worse. It was the last day of childhood.

GLOSSARY

1 *Martha*: Mrs Brennan, Baba's mother.

2 *Declan*: Baba's younger brother.

3 *Hickey*: the man who works for Caithleen's mother.

4 *hurley*: Irish form of hockey.

5 *the scholarship*: Caithleen has just learned that she has won a scholarship to a convent school.

6 *East Lynne*: a popular Victorian melodrama based on the novel by Mrs Henry Wood.

SUGGESTIONS FOR WRITING AND DISCUSSION

1 *Comment on some of the details about people's appearance and the countryside that the narrator (Caithleen) notices. What does this suggest about her?*
2 *What impression do you get of the kind of community this extract is set in?*
3 *Describe Caithleen's reaction to the news of her mother's death.*
4 *Comment on the things in this extract which show that Caithleen is still to a large extent a child.*
5 *Why does Caithleen say 'It was the last day of childhood'?*
6 *Write a story in which someone hears about an accident to a member of his or her family.*
7 *Read again carefully Edna O'Brien's description of a summer evening, the audience and the concert (note particularly how she describes people). Try your own account of a local event, perhaps the school play, or a concert or disco, or match that you have been to.*
8 *The characters in this extract react to the news of the death in different ways. What do you think is the best way of comforting someone who has lost a relative or loved one? (For instance, should you try to get them to think of something else? Let them talk? Help with chores that need doing? Talk to them of things you remember about the dead person? Pray with them?) Do you think funerals, wreath-laying, wakes have an important psychological function?*
9 *Notice the way in which Edna O'Brien brings her characters alive by simple but vivid descriptions of what they do and say. Write a description of your family and your neighbourhood for an outsider.*

FURTHER READING

The Country Girls Edna O'Brien (Penguin)
The Lonely Girl Edna O'Brien (Penguin)
Girls in Their Married Bliss Edna O'Brien (Penguin)

EARLE BIRNEY

Earle Birney was born in
Calgary, Canada, in 1904. He
studied at the University of
British Columbia and later
became Professor of English
there. He spent his childhood in
the mountainous regions of
Alberta and British Columbia,
the background for the poem
'David'. In the preface to his
Selected Poems Birney states
that the poem was rejected
fourteen times before being
published. It is now very popular
in school anthologies in Canada,
though not one of the poet's own
favourites. His autobiography,
Spreading Times, was published
in 1980.

DAVID

I

David and I that summer cut trails on the survey,
All week in the valley for wages, in air that was steeped
In the wail of mosquitoes, but over the sunalive week-ends
We climbed, to get from the ruck of the camp, the surly

Poker, the wrangling, the snoring under the fetid
Tents, and because we had joy in our lengthening coltish
Muscles, and mountains for David were made to see over,
Stairs from the valleys and steps to the sun's retreats.

II

Our first was Mount Gleam. We hiked in the long afternoon
To a curling lake and lost the lure of the faceted
Cone in the swell of its sprawling shoulders. Past
The inlet we grilled our bacon, the strips festooned

On a poplar prong, in the hurrying slant of the sunset.
Then the two of us rolled in the blanket while round us the cold
Pines thrust at the stars. The dawn was a floating
Of mists till we reached to the slopes above timber, and won

To snow like fire in the sunlight. The peak was upthrust
Like a fist in a frozen ocean of rock that swirled
Into valleys the moon could be rolled in. Remotely unfurling
Eastward the alien prairie glittered. Down through the dusty

Skree[1] on the west we descended, and David showed me
How to use the give of shale for giant incredible
Strides. I remember, before the larches' edge,
That I jumped a long green surf of juniper flowing

Away from the wind, and landed in gentian and saxifrage
Spilled on the moss. Then the darkening firs
And the sudden whirring of water that knifed down a fern-hidden
Cliff and splashed unseen into mist in the shadows.

III

One Sunday on Rampart's arête[2] a rainsquall caught us,
And passed, and we clung by our blueing fingers and bootnails
An endless hour in the sun, not daring to move
Till the ice had steamed from the slate. And David taught me

How time on a knife-edge can pass with the guessing of fragments
Remembered from poets, the naming of strata beside one,
And matching of stories from schooldays. . . . We crawled astride
The peak to feast on the marching ranges flagged

By the fading shreds of the shattered stormcloud. Lingering
There it was David who spied to the south, remote,
And unmapped, a sunlit spire on Sawback, an overhang
Crooked like a talon. David named it the Finger.

That day we chanced on the skull and the splayed white ribs
Of a mountain goat underneath a cliff-face, caught
On a rock. Around were the silken feathers of hawks.
And that was the first I knew that a goat could slip.

IV

And then Inglismaldie. Now I remember only
The long ascent of the lonely valley, the live
Pine spirally scarred by lightning, the slicing pipe
Of invisible pika,[3] and great prints, by the lowest

Snow, of a grizzly.[4] There it was too that David
Taught me to read the scroll of coral in limestone
And the beetle-seal in the shale of ghostly trilobites,[5]
Letters delivered to man from the Cambrian[6] waves.

V

On Sundance we tried from the col[7] and the going was hard.
The air howled from our feet to the smudged rocks
And the papery lake below. At an outthrust we balked
Till David clung with his left to a dint in the scarp,[8]

Lobbed the iceaxe over the rocky lip,
Slipped from his holds and hung by the quivering pick,
Twisted his long legs up into space and kicked
To the crest. Then grinning, he reached with his freckled wrist

And drew me up after. We set a new time for that climb.
That day returning we found a robin gyrating
In grass, wing-broken. I caught it to tame but David
Took and killed it, and said, 'Could you teach it to fly?'

VI

In August, the second attempt, we ascended The Fortress,
By the forks of the Spray we caught five trout and fried them
Over a balsam fire. The woods were alive
With the vaulting of mule-deer and drenched with clouds all the morning,

Till we burst at noon to the flashing and floating round
Of the peaks. Coming down we picked in our hats the bright
And sunhot raspberries, eating them under a mighty
Spruce, while a marten moving like quicksilver scouted us.

VII

But always we talked of the Finger on Sawback, unknown
And hooked, till the first afternoon in September we slogged
Through the musky woods, past a swamp that quivered with frog-song,
And camped by a bottle-green lake. But under the cold

Breath of the glacier sleep would not come, the moon-light
Etching the Finger. We rose and trod past the feathery
Larch, while the stars went out, and the quiet heather
Flushed, and the skyline pulsed with the surging bloom

Of incredible dawn in the Rockies. David spotted
Bighorns[9] across the moraine[10] and sent them leaping
With yodels the ramparts redoubled and rolled to the peaks,
And the peaks to the sun. The ice in the morning thaw

Was a gurgling world of crystal and cold blue chasms,
And seracs[11] that shone like frozen saltgreen waves.
At the base of the Finger we tried once and failed. Then David
Edged to the west and discovered the chimney;[12] the last

Hundred feet we fought the rock and shouldered and kneed
Our way for an hour and made it. Unroping we formed
A cairn on the rotting tip. Then I turned to look north
At the glistening wedge of giant Assiniboine, heedless

Of handhold. And one foot gave. I swayed and shouted.
David turned sharp and reached out his arm and steadied me,
Turning again with a grin and his lips ready
To jest. But the strain crumbled his foothold. Without

A gasp he was gone. I froze to the sound of grating
Edge-nails and fingers, the slither of stones, the lone
Second of silence, the nightmare thud. Then only
The wind and the muted beat of unknowing cascades.

VIII

Somehow I worked down the fifty impossible feet
To the ledge, calling and getting no answer but echoes
Released in the cirque, and trying not to reflect
What an answer would mean. He lay still, with his lean

Young face upturned and strangely unmarred, but his legs
Splayed beneath him, beside the final drop,
Six hundred feet sheer to the ice. My throat stopped
When I reached him, for he was alive. He opened his grey

Straight eyes and brokenly murmured, 'Over . . . over.'
And I, feeling beneath him a cruel fang
Of the ledge thrust in his back, but not understanding,
Mumbled stupidly, 'Best not to move,' and spoke

Of his pain. But he said, 'I can't move. . . . If only I felt
Some pain.' Then my shame stung the tears to my eyes
As I crouched, and I cursed myself, but he cried,
Louder, 'No, Bobbie! Don't ever blame yourself.

I didn't test my foothold.' He shut the lids
Of his eyes to the stare of the sky, while I moistened his lips
From our water flask and tearing my shirt into strips
I swabbed the shredded hands. But the blood slid

From his side and stained the stone and the thirsting lichens,
And yet I dared not lift him up from the gore
Of the rock. Then he whispered, 'Bob, I want to go over!'
This time I knew what he meant and I grasped for a lie

And said, 'I'll be back here by midnight with ropes
And men from the camp and we'll cradle you out.' But I knew
That the day and the night must pass and the cold dews
Of another morning before such men unknowing

The ways of mountains could win to the chimney's top.
And then, how long? And he knew . . . and the hell of hours
After that, if he lived till we came, roping him out.
But I curled beside him and whispered, 'The bleeding will stop.

You can last.' He said only, 'Perhaps. . . . For what? A wheelchair,
Bob?' His eyes brightening with fever upbraided me.
I could not look at him more and said, 'Then I'll stay
With you.' But he did not speak, for the clouding fever.

I lay dazed and stared at the long valley,
The glistening hair of a creek on the rug stretched
By the firs, while the sun leaned round and flooded the ledge,
The moss, and David still as a broken doll.

I hunched to my knees to leave, but he called and his voice
Now was sharpened with fear. 'For Christ's sake push me over!
If I could move . . . or die. . . .' The sweat ran from his forehead,
But only his eyes moved. A hawk was buoying

Blackly its wings over the wrinkled ice.
The purr of a waterfall rose and sank with the wind.
Above us climbed the last joint of the Finger
Beckoning bleakly the wide indifferent sky.

Even then in the sun it grew cold lying there. . . . And I knew
He had tested his holds. It was I who had not. . . . I looked
At the blood on the ledge, and the far valley. I looked
At last in his eyes. He breathed, 'I'd do it for you, Bob.'

IX

I will not remember how nor why I could twist
Up the wind-devilled peak, and down through the chimney's empty
Horror, and over the traverse alone. I remember
Only the pounding fear I would stumble on It

When I came to the grave-cold maw of the bergschrund[13] . . . reeling
Over the sun-cankered snowbridge, shying the caves
In the nêvé[14] . . . the fear, and the need to make sure It was there
On the ice, the running and falling and running, leaping

Of gaping greenthroated crevasses, alone and pursued
By the Finger's lengthening shadow. At last through the fanged
And blinding seracs I slid to the milky wrangling
Falls at the glacier's snout, through the rocks piled huge

On the humped moraine, and into the spectral larches,
Alone. By the glooming lake I sank and chilled
My mouth but I could not rest and stumbled still
To the valley, losing my way in the ragged marsh.

I was glad of the mire that covered the stains, on my ripped
Boots, of his blood, but panic was on me, the reek
Of the bog, the purple glimmer of toadstools obscene
In the twilight. I staggered clear to a firewaste,[15] tripped

And fell with a shriek on my shoulder. It somehow eased
My heart to know I was hurt, but I did not faint
And I could not stop while over me hung the range
Of the Sawback. In blackness I searched for the trail by the creek

And found it. . . . My feet squelched a slug and horror
Rose again in my nostrils. I hurled myself
Down the path. In the woods behind some animal yelped.
Then I saw the glimmer of tents and babbled my story.

I said that he fell straight to the ice where they found him.
And none but the sun and incurious clouds have lingered
Around the marks of that day on the ledge of the Finger,
That day, the last of my youth, on the last of our mountains.

GLOSSARY
1 *Skree*: mountain slope covered with small stones that slide down when trodden on.
2 *arête*: sharp ridge of mountain.
3 *pika*: small mammal like a small-eared rabbit.
4 *grizzly*: North American bear.
5 *trilobite*: fossil.
6 *Cambrian*: earliest geological period of organized life.
7 *col*: depression in mountain chain.
8 *scarp*: steep slope.
9 *Bighorns*: Rocky Mountains sheep.
10 *moraine*: debris carried down and deposited by glacier.

11 *seracs*: castellated masses into which a glacier is divided at steep points by the crossing of crevasses.
12 *chimney*: narrow cleft in a cliff-face.
13 *bergschrund*: crevasse at junction of steep upper slope with a glacier.
14 *névé*: expanse of snow not yet compressed into ice at the head of a glacier.
15 *firewaste*: a stretch of land burnt to serve as a firebreak.

SUGGESTIONS FOR WRITING AND DISCUSSION

1 *How does the poet convey the pleasure Bob and David take in the open-air life and physical activity?*
2 *What does Bob learn from David?*
3 *What are Bob's feelings for David?*
4 *Explain the tragic predicament Bob finds himself in and how he resolves it.*
5 *Why did David want to die?*
6 *If you had been in Bob's place, what would you have done?*
7 *Why does Bob say that day was 'the last of my youth'?*
8 *Comment on the effectiveness of 'David' as a narrative poem.*
9 *Write a story about someone who has to make a difficult decision.*
10 *Read Birney's account of expeditions he went on with David (sections II–VI). Notice his care about details to do with the landscape, plants and wildlife. Describe – in prose or verse – an expedition or outing you have been on with one or two good friends.*
11 *Write about a close friend whom you admire and who has taught you skills you did not have before.*
12 *Write about, or give a short talk on, a hobby or special interest of yours (for example, canoeing, riding, working with greyhounds, helping run a stall at your local market, bird watching, break dancing, playing an instrument).*

FURTHER READING

Collected Poems Vols I and II Earle Birney (McClelland & Stewart)

GENERAL SUGGESTIONS FOR WRITING AND DISCUSSION

1 *Write about two pieces of writing which give you an insight into what growing up is like in other countries or at other times.*

2 *Write about two pieces of writing which reminded you most vividly of your own childhood.*

3 *Choose three pieces of writing that you enjoyed reading and explain what it was about them that you particularly enjoyed.*

4 *Choose two or three of the characters portrayed here that have interested you and describe them.*

5 *Judging from the extracts you have read, would you say that childhood is a happy time or a sad time?*

6 *Take a character from one of the extracts and write your own story in which they play an important part (for example, Rosalie in 'Rosalie', Leo in 'Lost', Masha Miovic or Fishwala in 'The Mutilations of Saleem', Kaiser or Alan in 'The Marbleus', Leo or Danny in 'What's It Like To Be Jewish?').*

7 *Not only the famous write autobiographies. Write your own autobiography. You could use 'chapter' headings such as 'My Earliest Memories', 'First Day at School', 'Friends', 'My Family', 'A Special Occasion', 'Something Happy, Something Sad', 'The Best Day of My Life', 'The Worst Day of My Life', 'Myself', 'The Future'. You could write parts in prose and perhaps one or two sections – or parts of sections – as poems.*

8 *The poems 'A Tropical Childhood', 'Dives', 'Death of a Naturalist' and 'The Barn' deal with different experiences of childhood based, in each case, on the poet's own life. Choose one as a guide, or model, for your own poem about childhood.*

9 *Compare Miss Cooke in 'Moving Up', or Mr Zagallo in 'The Mutilations of Saleem', with someone who has taught you and whom you particularly remember.*